I'M AFRAID OF HYPNOSIS
BUT
I DON'T KNOW WHY

Answers the questions
YOU ALWAYS ASK

Deborah Marshall-Warren
edited by Peter B. Lloyd

Whole-Being Books, London.

I'm Afraid of Hypnosis but I Don't Know Why

Published by Whole-Being Books, an imprint of Ursa Software Ltd, 155 Sumatra Road, London NW6 1PN, England (www.ursasoft.com/publish). First trade paperback edition published 2003.

Set by Ursa Software Ltd. Printed by Biddles Ltd, Woodbridge Park Estate, Woodbridge Road, Guildford, Surrey GU1 1DA (www.biddles.co.uk).

Cover design by themediapractice.co.uk.

Other works published by Whole-Being Books:
Interactive Hypnotherapy: A Practical Training Manual

Author's note:

The names and some of the circumstances of all clients mentioned herein have been altered in order to preserve their confidentiality

ISBN: 1-902987-07-1

For
the subconscious

"I love my subconscious. My subconscious is like an angel.
It helps me all the time. Wonderful stories. Wonderful
memories. Wonderful designs for my life. I respect it,
and I thank it very much. I thank it for the wonderful
relationship we have and the companionship. It has opened
the door and was ready to give me the answers."

— a client

Throughout the book — for the sake of simplicity and consistency, reference is made to the practitioner as 'she' and the client as 'he'. An exception is made in specifically female case studies.

Acknowledgements

I did not make a conscious decision to become a hypnotherapist. I will categorically say that I was guided every step of the way. When I started out, eight years ago, I had no idea that people were afraid of hypnotherapy. Even my friends were 'afraid' of my 'change of heart' and change of direction. I had changed. I had decided to follow my heart.

God most certainly had a huge say in putting me onto this path, and keeping me on it. God surely knew that I was afraid too! On most days in that first couple of years, I sat in a small church and asked for help, and some days a thought popped in. It may be to write a letter, or to make a call. However small or seemingly remote the suggestion, I always followed through. There were many days when no one called, and some days when there was one call. I would arrive home and report on my dismal day. Peter would rally me with incredible enthusiasm. "One call, Deb! That's an upward trend! There'll be two tomorrow!" It was impossible not to laugh, and to count my blessings. His editorial expertise has worked wonders. Thanks also to Helen, and my mother, Margaret Rose for proof reading.

Eight years later, I count my phenomenal clients and thank them for the contribution that the warp and weft of their lives has made on fashioning my understanding of the complex tapestry of life as a hypnotherapist. It is a life that has woven of itself, over the last eight years a strong fabric of belief in the extraordinary potential of hypnotherapy. How awesome and how liberating hypnotherapy can be!

Just as I was guided, it sometimes seems that my clients are guided. They will say things like, "It's the first time I've bought *that* magazine", or "I just opened it at the page with your number." Friends are messengers, messengers are friends. Thank you all for coming and especially thanks for trusting. I am honoured to have met you and been part of your unfolding journeys.

I have to thank Luigia for the title of the book. Luigia arrived at our home in London in January 2002, as a student of English. Peter and I were to be her host parents for the succeeding months. One evening we were sitting around the kitchen table and she ventured to ask, "Deborah, do you think I could be hypnotised?" Immediately followed by, "Deborah, you know something? I'm afraid of hypnosis but I don't know why."

And finally, for the cover, I am indebted to the Timothy Taylor Gallery, London, to Terry Danziger Miles, and to Laurence Tuhey, who have both liaised with the owner, of *The Hypnotist* painting by David Hockney, on my behalf. Your contributions and the painting are wonderful and much appreciated gifts. It is as if the encounter with *The Hypnotist* has taken me on a remarkable journey, and unleashed a remarkable string of events, from alpha to Zabbar! David Hockney, I thank you too. And now, on with the Show! Or, rather, on with the Session! Enjoy!

Author's Prologue

◎   "I don't understand why everyone doesn't do this."

This book, *I'm Afraid of Hypnosis but I Don't Know Why* reveals the truth about hypnotherapy, and puts forward a clear and constructive message about the power of interactive hypnotherapy as a means of overcoming psychological challenges and enhancing your life.   First and foremost, the book offers guidance and support to all those readers who are considering embarking on a course of hypnotherapy, and are seeking a firmer grasp of what is involved; and those whose role it is to advise people about possible forms of therapy. I have found that clients tend to make a lot of enquiries, and talk to a lot of people, before choosing to follow through with this surprisingly enjoyable experience. *I'm Afraid of Hypnosis but I Don't Know Why* provides answers to commonly asked questions that people pose, both before and after a one-to-one session of hypnotherapy.

Regardless of whether you are seeking information about hypnotherapy for yourself, or on behalf of someone else — or are just curious — the basic ideas and information are of considerable importance to understanding the whole process of changing your mind for the better. You will discover that you can get help for a problem that you may have been putting up with for years. And you will get a clearer idea of what actually happens during a course of hypnotherapy sessions, and gain more insight into the role of the hypnotherapist. If you decide to choose hypnotherapy, this information will enable you to arrive at your session with an informed understanding of what hypnosis is, and what your therapeutic hypnosis will be like. Rest assured that you are not at risk of acting like an ass!

I'm Afraid of Hypnosis but I Don't Know Why, is a book about interactive hypnotherapy — not *the* definitive book about it. I am well aware that fellow practitioners will have different perspectives, although I hope they will nevertheless find much that is of interest in it. They will of course have their own views on interactive hypnotherapy, and will bring to the subject their own interests, background, perceptions, and skills. Please be aware that your hypnotherapist — by listening to, and trusting, her own intuition — may introduce other steps and may design your session in a different way. Many different sequences of steps can take you to where you want to be. The interactive and therapeutic, dance between both client and therapist is always in motion.

I'm Afraid of Hypnosis but I Don't Know Why also addresses the needs and interests of those in training, as well as practising therapists, and stress-management consultants. Indeed, all those who practise techniques of direct suggestion as part of their therapeutic repertoire, or who use relaxation and visualisation exercises, may find here techniques that will help them. They may find pointers for moving towards a more interactive approach.

Here are the words of a client reflecting on his experience of hypnosis by direct suggestion: "I sat and listened for twenty minutes to a prepared script. It didn't dent the surface. Nice words, but they went over the top. I didn't feel them inside me. I came away, and afterwards felt no difference". Contrast that with the same client's experience of interactive hypnotherapy: "I feel much more confident about it! There is nothing pushy about it. It's a bit of a wonderment. It gives me so much food for thought, and that in itself is good. The words stay there, and you can feed on them."

Primarily this is a book about hypnotherapy, and specifically interactive hypnotherapy. *I'm Afraid of Hypnosis but I Don't Know Why* is not a book about basic hypnotic techniques. There are as many excellent texts in the field of hypnosis and hypnotherapy as there are visualisation techniques. By way of illustration, however, the book does feature a sample induction, a deepener, and a sample interactive hypnotherapy session — to put the content in context. The focus of the book rests on what you can do with those tools, not on the tools themselves.

This book blows away the miasma of myths that surround hypnotherapy — a complementary therapy that is ripe for demystification and full respectability. *I'm Afraid of Hypnosis but I Don't Know Why* invites you to join the increasing number of people who come to hypnosis because they want something that is "positive, constructive and specific."

1

WHY NOT?

Your first approach to hypnotherapy

- "I associate it with stage hypnosis."
- "I associate it with phobias."
- "There's not enough knowledge about it."
- "There's a lot of ignorance and a little bit of fear."
- "It's completely alien to me."
- "It's kind of a weird thing to do. You don't know what's going to come out."

Now hypnotherapy is gaining respect. More and more people are attracted to hypnotherapy as something that can help personal development and growth. It is one of the most powerful, and yet somehow most misunderstood, of the complementary therapies in the lexicon of possibilities. Until recently, hypnotherapy has continued to be viewed with consumer suspicion. Vague feelings of fear and apprehension deterred people from trying it. Now, at long last, more and more people are opening their minds to a therapeutic technique that is enjoyable, relaxing and really very effective.

Many healthy and happy people say that "In every *other* part of my life, I am happy with who I am. I simply want help getting on top of one thing...", such as ... "public speaking", "an interview", "my driving test", "smoking", "unhealthy eating", "nail biting", "going red in front of authority figures", "being in high places", "not believing I can succeed in my competitive sport", "my loss of self-motivation", "lacking enough confidence to realise my full potential", "cutting out like a car that won't start, when I'm at an audition".

Some come to hypnotherapy because their usually healthy minds suddenly become *un*healthy. The bottom can appear to drop out of their respective worlds. Their usual buoyancy, happiness, and their robust sense of self-esteem sink without trace.

◎ "I split up with my partner."

◎ "I was made redundant and my confidence went."

◎ "My mum died."

◎ "My father passed away."

◎ "I started feeling anxious for no reason at all."

◎ "Things just got too busy at work, and I'm not handling the stress"

◎ "I started having nightmares."

◎ "I started feeling angry for no apparent reason."

◎ "I'm on a self-mending mission."

◎ "Ever since that happened, I've been feeling low."

Sometimes people come after they have taken some form of allopathic medication for a while — usually anti-depressants. They may be taking herbal self-medication such as St. John's wort. Or they come after they have been in counselling or psychotherapy of some kind, and perhaps are still there. They may have heard that interactive hypnotherapy can help take that process into the fast track, and get them off the cathartic couch, or comfy armchair, and back behind the driving seat of their lives. They come to get off the medication[1]. They come to get free.

And others come because it is the right time, and they are ready to understand more about themselves — to understand "how I've got like this," and to develop and evolve their emotional lives. Opportunity knocks, and reveals a chance to reconcile some of the key events of their lives that until now had been left unresolved. And there are those who use interactive hypno-therapy as a power tool. Such people may be practising meditators, or students of a personal or spiritual development path; or working and writing their way through a structured path such as *The Artist's Way*. If you are in that last category, then, you might, in the course of your self-explorations find yourself at an impasse in your journey. You may report feeling "stuck" or "blocked". All you need is a push — towards the light at the end of the tunnel. You know that with a little help from a co-facilitator — to help you flick a few switches, to gain more clarity and illumination — you can get on and continue the work yourself.

Interactive hypnotherapy presents different opportunities to different people. Generally speaking, if you can think of it, if you can put a name to it, you can use hypnotherapy to help clear

---

[1] In consultation with the responsible medical doctor.

it, to free it, to transform it, or to improve it! Do come with a sense of what you want to achieve. The clearer you can get your sense about your desired outcome, the better. Think of the outcome in terms of how you want to be and feel at the end of the process. This is not always easy. Granted, it is often much easier to declare what you do not want, and much more difficult sometimes to define with absolute assurance what you do. Having just some notion of what you want to achieve is fine, given that your desired change may — as you think about it right now — seem rather alien to how you have become accustomed to feeling or behaving. Trust your subconscious to come up with the why and the wherefore, and your therapist's skill in enabling you to make the change. Chapter 12, *Are You Sitting Comfortably?* provides more clarification, and reassurance in this area. Do bear in mind that, with even a vague agenda, you can still move towards what you want to get out of hypnotherapy and make the journey worthwhile.

There is so much acknowledgement and celebration of the potential of complementary therapies, and so much positive acceptance of the everyday use of 'alternatives' by the public and the media. It is surprising to find that an especially potent therapy — hypnotherapy — has not been honoured, acknowledged, and advanced enough to let its potential to benefit people in society at large be realised fully.

Hypnotherapy is often regarded as a last resort. It's something you try in desperation when you have already gone down all the other roads. After you have subjected yourself to other practices, after you have been in therapy on and off for years, and still not fathomed the problem or the challenge that you are facing. "...only then would I consider going to such lengths as hypnotherapy," as one client confided to me.

Chatting after a hypnotherapy session, a client will often express amazement at how easy and effortless the hypnotherapy had been. He may begin to wonder why hypnotherapy was not his first port of call. Invariably a client will say something along the lines of, "I've considered doing this for quite a while", or "I've been thinking about this on and off for ages."

Clients have often been put off by what they have seen of stage and television hypnosis; others say they just didn't know which hypnotherapist to choose and they didn't know anyone else who had tried hypnotherapy — and they didn't want to pick someone unknown from a directory. "It's a bit of a jungle", re-marked one client on the telephone. "You don't know who to go to, because you hear such funny things in the press about hypnosis."

Whatever you come to hypnotherapy to achieve, you will also find that your sense of self-confidence and self-esteem soars. This tends to happen even if you are not specifically aiming to boost your confidence. There is a welcome ripple effect into other areas of your life. Hypnotherapy truly is a way of helping you to gain your wings and to fly high. It is a way of discovering and ex-periencing your true colours.

Interactive hypnotherapy enables you literally to 'change your mind' or to 'make up your mind' for the better. You can change it, and make it up, to reflect the best and the brightest you can possibly be.

2
◎

Help, I Need Hypnotherapy!
The specific benefits of hypnotherapy

The decision to embark on hypnotherapy often arises from an awareness that something is affecting your day-to-day happiness, something is disturbing you, and that some help is needed to enable you to move forward and overcome whatever this challenge is.

We often do not know ourselves as well as we think we do, and strive to find out more. We may have a work C.V. (*curriculum vitae*, or résumé), which is right up to date, while holding on to an emotional C.V. stuck in the past. We may thus be unaware of our own emotional strengths, achievements and inner riches.

We are in touch with the world, but out of touch with ourselves. We communicate across the globe on mobile telephones, but sometimes we cannot communicate with our own selves. We can access understanding and knowledge at the push of a few buttons, but have not the understanding and knowledge to soothe and heal our own psychological buttons. We have pain buttons, grief buttons, irritation buttons, 'being misunderstood' buttons, 'let-down' and 'betrayed' buttons, rejection buttons. Often so raw, they're extremely sensitive when pushed. They can niggle, ache

11

and brood. Emotionally, people may 'stew in their own juice', 'fly off the handle', 'storm' out of a boardroom. Their text messages can trick instead of treat. Their emails flame and flare. Their voicemail messages fry with frustration. On the road, they are in a rage! At home, they lash out at loved ones.

Other people press your buttons the wrong way. That is when you react the most and may surprise yourself. When we choose to think about it, we may realise that our buttons are sometimes easily rendered hyper-sensitive. We may be irritated by people who make us wait as they rush through their days. These are situations that we may know all too well — the driver who doesn't drive fast enough for our schedule; the endlessly stopping refuse truck; or the home-removals van blocking our way in our own street; the irritatingly long queue; the person paying by cheque instead of a credit card or ready cash — people going about their business, sometimes too easily make us sore.

In new relationships with friends and lovers we discover more mental buttons. These buttons go by names like guilt, abandonment, rejection, failure, and being unloved. Whatever name you give them, they take root, and become over-sensitive. They can control you — at least, until you take control of them.

Consider three emotions.

1) Think of *Anger* as endlessly eating. And, however much she eats, she never feels full. She never feels fulfilled. You begin to take control when you start to question why. Why do I eat so much? It's not necessarily that you eat too much of the 'bad

stuff'. In fact, you might not be eating the bad stuff at all. You may be eating too much of the nutritional good stuff. The problem is simply that you just cannot stop eating.

Alternatively, in some cases, Anger may do the opposite: she may refuse to eat at all.

2) *Guilt* may drink excessive amounts of alcohol or take drugs until she is out of your mind. Your inner judge may engage you in dialogue at any time of day or night, making its judgements and bringing forward the inner voices that express worry, fear, anxiety, guilt or regret. Those voices can lead to insomnia, as they do not need sleep. They are players who play on your mind, and can imprison you with their chains of words. They can prevent you from getting on with your life in a way that honours who you truly are.

3) Sometimes *Anger* and *Guilt* are so afraid, and so ashamed of what they might do if they were ever to be unleashed — that each of them can cause you much unease and so, indirectly, dis-ease. They can make you feel small, and make you cower. They themselves cower anxiously. Then *Anxiety* holds the reins to your days: *Anxiety* pulls the strings. For, *Anxiety* does not let you live a normal life. But *Anger* and *Guilt* are by no means the only rogue players fuelling the anxious mind. *Anxiety*'s diet is a banquet. It is a feast that consists of your life — all the first-times, the fearful times, the embarrassed times, the humiliated times, the misunderstood times and the wronged times. *Anxiety* finds succour in the many different rites of

passage that we experience in our growing-up. And of course we are always growing up. These events and situations are just the ones that we especially remember. Rarely have we completely forgotten the others. Our awareness may consist of a vague recollection perhaps. We have lost sight, sense, and sound of the fine details, but the essence persists.

We live in an age of anxiety and uncertainty. Anxiety is like a modern-day virus. Anxiety can attack completely out of the blue. The eruption of anxiety in the form of a panic attack is increasingly common. Panic attacks do not announce themselves. They are downright rude. They barge in, and take over when you would least expect them to turn up. You could be out and about — in a shopping centre, on holiday in the sun, feeling happy and relaxed, or travelling on a train, a bus, or an aeroplane.

People who speak about their experiences of panic attacks generally report the experiences as being very frightening — their personal diagnosis is often described as "I thought I was having a heart attack", or "I thought I was going to die". Suddenly the buttons are pressed full on — all survival stations are put on red alert.

People who experience panic attacks, and people who fear flying, or lizards, have much in common. Collectively they do not know the reason for the sudden impulse of emotion or behaviour. They do not know what lies behind the veil. Part of their response is inevitably a fear of the unknown.

We may, at times, inflict these self-limiting beliefs upon ourselves by believing other people's opinions of ourselves.

"Your stammer is your personality. People have said that to me all of my life," acknowledged a male client.

As youngsters we are much more vulnerable to grown-ups' opinions. From those opinions we may derive both pleasure and pain at different times. Similarly, we are vulnerable to the effects of labels that others give us. Often repeated, these labels embed themselves in the subconscious mind. They become embedded either for the benefit of a child's developing personality, or in denial of the bright spirit within the child, which longs to shine.

In their formative years, children are under pressure to accept what they are given. Children are told to eat up all the food on their plates — to 'eat their greens'. Children can devour and absorb words even more effectively than dinner. Children eat whatever is given to them — whether it is a good apple or a poisoned apple — especially when served up by loved ones or protectors. Likewise they accept trustingly the verbal expressions that are given to them to digest and absorb. Their faculty for discerning what is an appropriate diet for their minds is limited by a lack of understanding and by an unconditional love. When diseased fruits land on her plate, the child may blame herself for the bad taste and sickness rather than the source of those fruits. Unable to separate the pea from the pod in her mind, she may not be able to formulate a clear idea of the external source of her unhappiness. A frequently repeated word can become a label that we wear as a hand-me-down wound — one that is still weeping in someone else — perhaps the label-givers themselves. When words are good, their effect can be very beneficial, and when they are bad they can be very, very bad. We ingest and digest them — as told to do so by parents and siblings at home, teachers and others at school — but discover later that some of them worked to hold back our growing mental self and to deny the potential to be who we truly are. The NSPCC's *Full Stop* campaign awakened fuller awareness of the words that are ejaculated in anger. Advertising posters on hoardings and bus stops screamed words that a child might be told, "You're thick. You're stupid. You're no child of mine."

The brightest spark in the heavens would need phenomenal strength, self-belief and determination, in order to transcend continual put-downs and hand-me-down labels. In fact we generally do muddle through, we get by to a lesser or greater degree. We have the strength, we have the seeds of self-belief. And we have determination. There are many bright sparks out there, who continue to transcend their received labels, and who strive to correct their initial social programming in some way each day — to work towards recognising the truth about themselves. Colin Powell, the American Secretary of State, grew up in the Bronx, the son of Jamaican immigrants coming to America in the conditions and political climate of the day. He said of his early years in life, "I was not going to let other people's opinions of me become my opinion of myself."

We do not all make it, all the way. Some of us need help — help in flicking a few switches, or releasing some locks, in the subconscious mind — to get us fully into the light at the end of the tunnel.

Hypnotherapy is a way to lift the bonnet of the inner engine, to give yourself a fuel change — to let go of any residual low-octane fuel, so that you can live a higher-performance life, and a more emotionally comfortable life. Yes, you may know about the original trigger event. But, what you may not know is how that event is fuelling your reactions and responses in the here and now. The surprises in a hypnotherapeutic session are quite often the 'links' and the 'connections' between the situations, circum-stances, and original trigger events that are revealed to be under-lying the problem. These are the surprises and, as such, can lead you to reflections at the end of the session, such as: "But ... I *knew* all about that happening. Yet, I'd no idea that it was affecting me in this way." It seems that your subconscious mind will alert you to what you are ready and open to receive.

Therapy and counselling have for years provided long-term answers. For many, it has offered a long-term commitment to a contract — a contract lasting anything from six weeks to six months, and sometimes years — once, twice or even three times a week. After completing that long-term contract, you may have ended your therapy with understanding — but no change, no transformation, and sometimes even feeling worse.

Talking can help, but it can do that without actually changing you. At worst, it indulges you, if it goes on beyond what is
worthwhile.   Bright and intelligent people can talk endlessly,
without the subconscious getting a word in edgeways.

As an example of this, here is Pearl and her story:

◎ "...eight years ago my boyfriend died. I was born and
raised in Africa. I came to England because my sister was
here. My sister bullied me until the age of twenty-three. It
stopped nine years ago. She used to be very controlling. I
want to hurt myself or punish myself all the time. My
sister is older. I admire my mother. She only drinks socially now. There's some forgiveness on my side. My
Father. Why was he giving her drink or inviting her to
drink? My sister too — her self-esteem is low. I now live
with my sister and her boyfriend. I spend three or four
days with them and then go to my boyfriend. I wish to
finish with him. Since I met him I went into a different
phase. I'm tense all of the time. I keep my mind busy. I
seem to do it with food — in an abusive way — or in a
physical relationship. I would like to be in a position
where I can do more. I need to start believing in myself. I
need to have more self-esteem — to know I can do it for
myself".

The subconscious does, however, listen.   And what it
listens to is a detailed story of what happened to you. By endlessly talking about what happened and why, you very effectively
install in your mind new versions of the same old stories (which
the mind uses as its software), affirming your fears and appre-
hensions. Sometimes when stories are told, they take on new

twists and variations. And when they are stories about pain ... well, put it this way: with no new characters or motifs, you write the same script!

Consider your subconscious as the hard disk of a computer. Until you install different software the computer will run the same program. This normally is what you want a computer to do. But, you come to therapy to do and feel something different — to change. For this to happen you need to change the software. To do that, first you need to access the old software and discover the flaws in the programming. Next, you have to design the new software, and then to write and to install it. Once it is loaded, you will experience yourself running in a different way. Is it really that simple? Believe me, yes!

Let us now discover how Pearl's new way of thinking began to emerge and to change. What follows are key extracts over three of a total of five sessions.

We will begin with the initial session. Pearl's subconscious was addressed in hypnosis.

"Subconscious, Pearl reports to me that she experiences low self-esteem. Subconscious, may I ask respectfully, what is the reason for the low self-esteem?"

"Being left out and not being considered as a person."

We find that, in a state of relaxation, bright, intelligent people will drop their diversionary digressions to such an extent that their deeper and knowing wisdom can, and often almost immediately does, succeed in getting key and illuminating utterances into the flow of conversation! Moreover, these key events and situations are communicated to the therapist as clipped and abbreviated verbal chunks, which nonetheless convey the situation or event that is revealing itself within. The terse form of the communication also serves to protect your privacy and allow for information to be conveyed to the therapist only at your discretion. This, by the way, refutes the myth that once you are under hypnosis, you will involuntarily tell the therapist all your secrets. In fact, you will tell the therapist only what you wish to reveal. Moreover, there is no need for the private details of your life to be spoken aloud. The method is a 'structural' one, in the sense that it engages with the structure of your beliefs and not with their content. All the beliefs and experiences can be thought of as being in mental files that are labelled with evocative names. Under hypnosis, the interactive dialogue with yourself, con-structive work can be done by referring to these files by labels or symbols assigned by you. When you privately open the mental files, the therapist does not necessarily need you to describe their contents. In order to respect your integrity, the content of many, and indeed possibly all of the files, may remain private. That decision will be entirely up to you, and is down to how you feel in the moment. Whether spoken aloud or privately, your interior words of wonder will hold an equal degree of potency that can reconcile and heal. If you choose not to speak about the specifics of the experience, then short fragments are nonetheless sufficient to identify the content that is being uncovered and handled. In the following transcripts from Pearl, notice how simple and direct the utterances have become. (The ellipsis, ..., indicates a pause, which is often an important part of the dialogue.)

Where are you? ... Where do you sense you are?

"In the living room. My mother is on the floor un-conscious. .... Until today, I didn't know what was happ-ening. My sister knew. They thought I was too young for them to tell me."

What needs to be in place for Pearl to include herself?

"Comfort."

Would you allow Comfort to come forward and speak?

The therapist then talks with Comfort, who agrees to ask the older Pearl to hug and comfort the younger Pearl. Then Comfort speaks:

"I'll tell her [referring to the young Pearl], it is okay. I'll tell her it is under control. I can really see Pearl [referring to the present Pearl] hugging the little child where she was. She would like to be noticed. She needs to be okay with herself — to do things by herself."

Comfort, I'd like you to embed that wisdom, as absolute commands — absolute commitments to Pearl — deep, deep, deeply down, in the very foundations of her inner mind. Take as long as it takes, and say 'yes' when you've done.

"Yes. I've done."

Subconscious how does that feel?

"Feels good."

Subconscious, would it be appropriate to invite Self-esteem forward to speak?

And so the session continued: embedding choice seeds of self-esteem and planting the suggestion that those seeds would grow.

In as few sessions as possible, clients want to feel comfortably in the land of the living — to be in the land of the free! They want to feel and live fully, and to experience being their true selves, as loved and loving human beings. They wish to be able to step out in life, learning from life, together with others. They want to captain their own 'inner team', and be a positive force for the good of other 'outer teams' they belong to — with their families, at work on their careers, or at play socially.

Pearl's story on the second session runs as follows:
"Somehow with the behaviour of my mother, I thought I couldn't get any better".
Subconscious, Pearl reports to me that she thought she couldn't get any better. Subconscious, may I respectfully ask, what is the reason for this thought form?
The reason came forward as Scared. Scared, following a process of discussion and negotiation, agreed to be dissolved and eliminated. Pearl's subconscious then reported feeling better and lighter.
What needs to be in place for Pearl to feel better and better, lighter and lighter?
"Needs courage."
Courage spoke:
"Something nice is going to happen to her. Something nice that can motivate her. Something nice that happens only to her."

Courage was invited to choose a companion team player to coach alongside herself, and to champion further Pearl's success. Courage chose Confidence as coach. So, Confidence agreed to play full out alongside Courage — to be a constant presence by her side:
"To step out with Courage. To coach Courage to begin to create nice things."

Here is Pearl's story as it had evolved by the third session:
"I have much more strength. I am more positive. I am less scared of the future. I can see a tiny, tiny light. I have been enjoying my own time — time on my own. Before, I used to panic. I would like to have more of a social life with people — at work and with my own friends. I'd like to get my driving licence."

Subconscious, Pearl reports to me she has experienced much more strength and positivity. What needs to be in place for strength and positivity to continue to grow — day after day after day?
"[She needs to] stop putting herself out."

Where are you? … Where do you sense you are?
"The place we used to go during weekends. My parents and sister. Parents are arguing — arguing about leaving each other."

What needs to be in place for Pearl to stop putting herself out?
"The bit that puts her down — to go."

What name does the bit that 'puts Pearl down' go by?
"No name — has been there a long time — a really long time."

The 'bit that put Pearl down', following a further process of discussion and negotiation, like that which revealed Scared in the previous session, agreed to be dissolved, and eliminated.

Subconscious, how does that feel?

"Feels nice and clean."

Subconscious, what needs to be in place for Pearl to feel nice and nicer, clean and cleaner?

"Recognition."

Recognition spoke:

"Make her more assertive. Have more character. Recognise her value and self worth. Learn how to say 'no', without feeling guilty. Not to have to explain."

As before, this championing influence was invited to choose another inner team player to come on board. Recognition chose Assertion to join Pearl's empowered and empowering inner team. Then Assertion agreed to play full-out together with Recognition:

"To say no without hesitation and without having to say why. To say no and not to be scared."

Pearl participated in two further interactive hypnotherapy sessions. The fifth culminated in her sensing herself, during hypnosis, getting into a car and driving. She was curious as to where the drive would take her, but nonetheless she felt herself very much in control — in the driving seat — behind the steering wheel — driving forward in her life.

So, how does it work? Basically, interactive hypnotherapy gets the conscious mind out of the way for a while, and allows the subconscious to come forward where it can be a source of fresh insight, ideas, and solutions. It does this through the state of relaxation called 'hypnosis'.

Ian Robertson is Professor of Psychology at Trinity College, Dublin. In his book *The Mind's Eye* he confirms:

> "Most of us can learn to use the power of our mind's eye without ever visiting a hypnotist. Because it is not the hypnotist who changes your brain — it is *you* who does."

Precisely how hypnosis works is still not known. That, however, does not mean we should doubt the efficacy of hypnosis. For, as researchers in cognitive psychology will readily admit, most of the mind's workings are still shrouded in mystery. Precisely how your mind carries out easy, everyday things such as walking, talking, and recognising faces, is just not known. Hypnosis is no more mysterious than how you wake up in the morning! It is really just a myth that hypnosis is more mysterious or enigmatic than any of the other everyday things your mind can do.

Hypnosis is essentially the same thing as self-hypnosis, in so far as the crucial ingredient is that the mind allows itself to relax. A hypnotherapist can neither make you go into the state of hypnosis, nor keep you in a state of hypnosis against your will. This fact promotes a strong feeling of security and self-confidence. It also decreases your dependence on the hypnotherapist and becomes an aid in learning self-hypnosis. Whatever method a hypnotherapist uses, the method will rely on your interest and willingness to be aided and guided into this deliciously altered state.

To some this 'state' will sound scary. The immediate response to the phrase 'altered states' may be apprehension, and fear that you will lose control. That fear is mistaken. In fact, you effectively gain control, getting into the driving seat of your mind, getting behind the controls and the steering wheel of your life.

In fact, you will discover in Chapter 3 that you are rather more used to doing this than you think. It is just that you do not always notice that you are doing it.

Interactive hypnotherapy is *specific* in that it allows you to access a key event, a specific situation that is 'feeding' your experience. The process lets you go directly to the specific 'file' that is influencing your experience of yourself right now, and open it and edit it. It might be an experience of being stuck and unable to move, or an experience of fear and anger, or an experience of lack — a lack of confidence, or of self-esteem. This is like being given the key to a storehouse of memorabilia. Over the years, I have saved my birthday cards; and I discovered that my father had saved those birthday cards for each year when I was too young to save them for myself. So now I can search through a folder with all of the birthday cards that I received on each birthday, and bring back the memories of that time. Regression, when it is used in fast-track therapy, lets you go back through your latent memories in the same way.

Fast-track interactive hypnotherapy can take you to specific influencing events and experiences in any particular year. You can go directly to the first day of school, when you felt abandoned, rejected, frightened, and insecure — having been left there by a parent whom you implored not to leave you. You can go directly to the eleven-year-old who overheard her parent's best friend comparing her with a sibling. You can go directly to the thirteenth year, to the teenager humiliated, and feeling dirty when she discovered she was bleeding. You can go directly to your seventeenth year to the young woman who submitted to a termination, and to this day has experienced a sense of guilt and shame and blushes for 'no apparent reason at all'. Of course you may say that you knew about each and every one of those events. What you may not have known is how that event has been impacting your life up to this point. Fay wanted each successive boyfriend to spend all of his spare time with her, a desire that naturally strained every relationship. In hypnosis Fay met her father and discovered that she was desirous of his time and attention too. Her father's response to young Fay's natural inclination to be with him was, "I can't spend all my time with you." Hypnotherapy can give you a sense of enlightenment and surprisingly immediate links with past and present personal circumstances. You gain accurate clarity, and understanding about what really happened. It can help foster another perspective. Constructively and positively, you discover that it was as painful and traumatic for your parent to leave you on that first day at school as it was for you. It did not mean that your parent was abandoning you. Your parent continued to love you all through that first day. The eleven-year-old 'ugly duckling' can meet her beautiful and successful 'swan'. She will be amazed, delighted and so happy to discover her.

Within the hypnosis, you can reassure, and assuage the fear and shock of, the emerging young woman within you, and speak to any peers or others who may have contributed to confusion on the first day you experienced menstruation. And to the seventeen-year-old, you can reassure her that she made the right decision at the time, and that if she had not made that decision then, she may not have been able to step through the doors which have opened for her now — be it a job, an opportunity, or a relationship. After the grieving, the way is open for the seventeen-year-old you to begin to grow up into her successful future, and for you to move forward into the future, free from looking forever at the past. With this new clarity and understanding comes freedom from the feelings of 'shame'. So the symptoms of blushing, which until now had unconsciously been fuelled by 'shame', will become less and less, and indeed may immediately disappear.

In talking with clients I often relate the following analogy. It is one that seems to make immediate sense. Each of us has a work CV or résumé, one that generally we keep up-to-date. In contrast, our emotional CV can get stuck way back in the past. In *Mind Detox* I wrote:

> Words and phrases oft-repeated, particularly before the age of ten, can become installed and ingrained like a reflex in your being, along with the associated thoughts. This

tightly bound knot of word and thought will be triggered whenever a similar situation crops up (however far removed), faithfully ensuring that the emotional responses run exactly as before. It will continue to rerun, until you rediscover this silent and invisible habit of thought in the background, echoing from some long-forgotten time earlier in your life.

Interactive hypnotherapy helps you update your emotional CV to the point that it runs concurrently with your work CV. You are likely then to stop looking back into a rear-view mirror of the past whilst driving forward into your successful future. You have accessed, and acquainted yourself with that which is lying dormant and waiting to be acknowledged and updated within. As if after a weeding and watering of your inner garden, you experience yourself immediately lighter and more fully alive to the present reality. You experience yourself stronger, and more confident. When you have more conscious understanding and clarity you have a real sense of 'healing' and liberation from the past.

3

◎

HYPNOTIC HYPE:

Don't believe everything you read about hypnosis!

◎ A theatre critic writes: "A superbly acted production — casts the hypnotic spell of a ghost story."

◎ A film critic writes: "...a hypnotic visual tapestry of the Irish mob in gangland Chicago that is to gangster movies what a Chanel label is to the rag business."

◎ An art critic writes: "The artist's work is stamped by a maternal warmth, a sentimental softness and an evocative quality that casts a spell and hypnotic trance."

◎ A journalist writes: "Having a baby... speaking in public... It's easy when you're under the spell".

◎ The copy-line in a car advertisement: "Streamline, stunning, hypnotic. (enough about the price, now let's look at the car.)"

Hypnotic spells and enchantments! The notion of the hypnotic a-bounds. So evocative and alluring is a whiff of the stuff, that a cosmetic company even named its perfume *Hypnotic*, to entrance potential customers!

The phrase 'hypnotic spell' is in common currency when describing encounters with performances and artistic talent that evoke awe and wonder in ourselves. And more recently in product advertising. But the currency is somewhat debased. For the idea of hypnosis having anything to do with casting magic spells is far removed from the truth. Yes, the results can be magical, but hypnosis is not magic. On the contrary, it is part of the warp and weft of the natural world! We have all been entranced by the notion of trance, and formed ideas and impressions about hypnosis that owe more to fancy than to reality. Many of our ideas ring true neither about how a state of hypnosis is induced today, nor about how it is used.

Although it is dismaying, it is not surprising that many people hold the dismissive or fearful view of hypnosis that they do. For, there are many examples in both the latest stories and the older cultural archives to colour one's view of hypnosis. The idea of 'hypnosis' has often been hi-jacked by purveyors of indoctrination, conditioning, and cultism, and then parodied by the entertainment industry. And further, hypnotherapy is the only complementary therapy which has its pivotal technique — hypnosis — employed outside of the therapeutic arena, be it on television or on stage as a form of entertainment.

When hypnosis was first discovered, both recreational and remedial trances were used in French aristocratic society. Then in England it became known amongst the Victorians, and was used to enchant and to entertain small groups of friends at social soirées, or séance gatherings. Trance has been written about in books, depicted on radio, film, and television, and in the latter part of the last century became tagged to dance. To help you remember how some of the seeds may have been sown within your inner mind, we will consider some of the messages you may have absorbed through different media over the years.

The film of Rudyard Kipling's Indian adventure stories, *The Jungle Book,* is etched in the memories of many and, as a classic animation film, is still watched by children and adults alike. Here, as in many other fictional accounts, the means of hypnotising someone is portrayed as being through the eyes alone. You may well remember the scene when Kaa, the python, hypnotises Bagheera, the black panther, in order to capture the man cub, Mowgli. In fact, the scene is completed with Disneyesque spirals in Kaa's eyes, which are mirrored by spinning spirals in the two victims' eyes. This popular idea may be based loosely on the real-life technique of 'fixed-gaze' induction, in which the subject is led into a state of focused relaxation by gazing constantly on some fixed point, such as the hypnotist's eyes. Yet, there is no special hypnotising power in the eyes. The eyes are just a convenient focal point.

The evolution of the mythic spiral shape is interesting in itself. The spiral as a decorative motif was designed in different localities around the world in the pre-historic past, amongst tribes with no contact with each other. In caves from Ireland to Malta, home to some of the world's oldest megalithic temples, the motif was a ubiquitous form of art and design in temple buildings. In particular, spirals were used to decorate strategically placed megaliths that acted as barriers, screens or blocking slabs restricting access to certain parts of the temple. Spiral forms were sometimes carefully executed with attention to measurements and pattern design. Like anything else in prehistoric culture, it is probably impossible to rediscover what meaning these spirals held for the early artists. How spirals found their way into the recent mythology of hypnosis I do not know, but we can certainly speculate whether it might be tapping into primeval archetypes.

Back to the cinema ... More than likely, you watched the Jungle Book when you were a child, at an age when you were most impressionable and absorbed sensory impressions like a sponge absorbs water. I am making an assumption here, but not an unreasonable one.

Did the belief that a hypnotist could hypnotise a person with the eyes alone seed somewhere in your subconscious? You may not remember the specific scene in the film, but you may well hold the belief that 'if you look into my eyes', you may well be hypnotised, 'and feel sleepy'.

If you have spent time in India, then you may well be familiar with books on hypnosis that do speak of the eyes as being the channel through which an hypnotic influence is exerted. Like the Indian snake-charming trick, the technique is not what it seems. As we saw earlier, the hypnotist's eyes are used as a focus for attention, and not as a channel for hypnotic energy. Even so, in contemporary western hypnotherapy I have yet to come across the eyes of the hypnotist ever being used as the focus for fixing attention. Certainly this is not an induction that I have ever used, nor seen demonstrated in training seminars by other experts in their field. Nor to the best of my knowledge is this induction technique used by my colleagues. I would be curious and intrigued to hear from those practitioners who do use the fixed gaze induction to facilitate the state of hypnosis. It is, I suspect, as mythical as the ubiquitous swinging pocket watch or the mantra "you are feeling sleepy — very ... very ... sleepy". Nevertheless, the swinging object still holds good as the conventional shorthand that signifies hypnosis in popular culture. In 2002, Motorola adopted a swinging mobile telephone in their poster campaign, beneath which read the copy line *Hypnomoto* (i.e. 'hypnotic Motorola'). Perhaps Motorola envisaged that their audience would be drawn to it, controlled by it, and compelled by an irrepressible desire to own it. Indeed even be hypnotised by it! Or, more likely, this was a knowing post-modern play on a universally recognised emblem. This was a mobile telephone whose hypnotic attraction could grip you in more ways than advertorial ones. Intrigued? Find out more in Chapter 4.

Moreover, this representation continues to be the standard way of presenting hypnosis in fiction. Lady Georgia Byng's novel for children, *Molly Moon's Incredible Book of Hypnotism* is an excellent yarn, which I would warmly recommend for kids to read. It appeals to children's yearning for freedom and adventure, whilst also tuning into the child's natural sense of caring and compassion for others. Unfortunately, it does also buy into the standard code for fictional hypnosis: namely, coercively hypnotising people through a power emanating from the eyes. After the book was published, two hypnotherapy bodies criticised the book for supposedly encouraging young children to hypnotise each other. As Lady Byng said in response, this is absurd. Of course, children will *play* at hypnotising one another, but as the book fails to explain the central role of deep relaxation in hypnosis, it is rather unlikely that they would ever succeed. The bigger danger is that those children will grow up thinking hypnosis is all about occult powers of the eyes and the voice; and that they may then miss out on the genuine benefits of hypnotherapy. If you do choose to lead your child to this book please explain that it does not present the whole truth about hypnosis as a therapy. The truth is much more empowering!

I do not want to reveal much of *Molly Moon*'s plot for you, but as you will gather from the title, it centres on a manual for doing hypnosis. This is the imaginary work *Hypnotism: An Ancient Art Explained*, written by Dr D. Logan and published in 1908. Dr Logan rightly says that "Trances are very normal things," that "Daydreaming is another form of entering a trance", and that the hypnotist works by giving suggestions to someone in trance, to stop smoking or "no longer feel afraid of riding in an automobile". After that, however, there is an increasing element of artistic licence.

Following the introductory section on self-hypnosis, a student of Dr Logan's book learns to hypnotise animals as a prelude to hypnotising humans. I will quote Dr Logan's instructions at length, as Georgia Byng has crystallised part of the popular mis-

apprehension of hypnosis as being something mysterious, border-
ing on the supernatural. "1. Go into a trance yourself. 2. [T]hink
of the animal … that you are going to hypnotise. Think about the
essence of that animal. Try to become that animal. 3. … Find the
'voice' that fits your animal. 4. Face your animal, slowly approach-
ing it if necessary. Think of the animal's 'voice' and now perform
it slowly and calmly. Repeat the animal's voice, in a lulling way,
until the animal becomes rocked into a trance. A pendulum may
be used. … Once the animal is in a trance, you will know it from
the "Fusion Feeling'". From Molly's subsequent actions we learn
that the method for hypnotising people is the same, although for
one-to-one hypnosis, it may be augmented with … slowly …
uttered … empathic … words … or a swinging pendulum, or both.

At no point does the hypnotist (a) ask for the subject's permission to embark on the hypnotic induction, or (b) invite the subject to participate voluntarily, or (c) ask the subject to collaborate
interactively in determining the aims of the hypnosis or the
suggestions to be employed to achieve those aims. This picture is
anchored firmly in the message that the hypnotic state is something that the hypnotist *imposes* on the subject, as opposed to real-
life hypnotherapy where the subject chooses to bring himself into
the hypnotic state at the *invitation* of the hypnotist. It is also
anchored in the limited form of hypnosis called direct suggestion,
as opposed to the more flexible and more potent participative
form.

One unusual item in Dr Logan's directions is the 'fusion feeling' that the hypnotist is supposed to feel when she and the subject are in trance together. This is another piece of pure fantasy as far as hypnosis is concerned, although it is curiously redolent of the feeling of union with nature that people report after deep meditation. It also hints at the reality that, in extended sessions of hypnotherapy, there may be a sense of communion with the client.

Georgia Byng does not quote Dr Logan on how the hypnotist's eyes actually convey their power, but dotted through the book are allusions to an electrostatic force. In one hypnotic battle with another girl, "she increased her voltage of glare to maximum power", and "it gave Molly a surge of energy. With a sizzling knock-out stare that made Molly's hair stand out from her head, the tension snapped and Molly had won," and in front of an audience, "Molly felt a surge of something like electricity in the air which made her tingle from head to toe. It was that fusion feeling, but on a massive scale." This is a novel twist on Franz Anton Mesmer's popular nineteenth-century theory of ' animal magnetism' (or 'zooelectricity' as Sir Richard Burton knew it), and it is a variation on the persistent myth that hypnosis involves some force — as opposed to it simply being a change of mental state.

It may seem fanciful to suppose that children's entertainment can engender widespread popular misconceptions about hypnosis among adults. So, let us look at one example of how the scaremongering is still taking hold today. An eleven-year-old boy arrived at my practice with his mother one day. Having introduced himself, he asked in a mock-menacing way "Where's your pocket watch?" Amused by his enchanting sense of drama, I informed him that I did not use a pocket watch. He took in the practice room with a sweeping look, glancing around for evidence of implements and said, "So what sinister method do you use to hypnotise people then?" Taken aback I asked him why he thought that hypnosis was 'sinister'. The answer lay with an extremely good storybook for children, *The Demon Headmaster*, written by Gillian Cross over twenty years ago.

The back cover of the current paperback edition features the demon headmaster's penetrating green luminescent eyes. The hypnotically governed school immediately strikes newcomers as unnatural:

> "I hope you are not going to be a person who won't co-operate with me." On the first day at her new school, Dinah realises something is horribly wrong. The children are strangely neat and well behaved; they even work during playtime. What makes them behave this way? What is the secret of the Headmaster's control?

The book's popularity was such that the BBC went on to dramatise this, and other books in the series. I thoroughly enjoyed the book, on the level of entertainment, but with my professional hat on I was aware that, in capturing the imagination of the young reader in this way, it was hypnosis that was defined and under-stood to be the instrument of control, rather than the dysfunctional ego of the headmaster. Hypnosis is the excuse for bad behaviour.

The same misconception is engendered by stage hypnosis, where hypnosis is used as the excuse for antics on stage, which is rather like blaming a football match for the rowdy behaviour of soccer hooligans. Hypnosis is a powerful and constructive instrument, which sometimes gets blamed for its misuse.

The *Demon Headmaster* books could be said to about cultism, brainwashing, and conditioning. Hypnosis has so often been tagged by all three catch phrases. The plot and incidents of the book invite several analogies. The book invokes comparison with the Hitler Youth movement formed of eight million children, brainwashed to believe they were members of the master race.

It was a culture of chilling obedience, and was embraced by children and young people of every class in 1930s Germany. Anyone who was not a member was portrayed as someone who did not fit in, who did not belong to the German people. Children were bullied into joining, or their schools threatened to expel them if they did not. Propaganda films showed the boys skiing, canoeing, boxing, horse riding, driving motor bikes — doing all the things that dreams are made of — tempting treats for a disadvantaged city boy who had never seen the countryside. There was obligatory 'sports duty' for the under-sixteens, pre-military training for the older ones who would go on to become stormtroopers. These war games were intentionally bruising. Any show of weakness or emotion was abhorred. The Hitler Youth marched everywhere, the boys, knobbly-kneed legions in tight lederhosen or brown shorts and shirt, black neckerchief with a swastika armband. The girls wore blue skirts and white blouses. The uniforms were intended to banish class and encourage leadership. Hitler's dictum that "youth must be led by youth" meant the concept of leadership and power was ceaselessly inculcated and became almost a fetish. Extracts from *The Demon Headmaster* beg comparison.

> There on the steps stood a row of six children, three boys and three girls. They were all tall and heavily built and they were marked out from the others by a large white P sewn on to their blazer pockets. Without smiling, the tallest girl took a pace forwards.
>
> 'Form — rows!' she yelled into the silence.
>
> 'Yes, Rose,' all the children said, in perfect unison. As quietly and steadily as marching soldiers, they walked together, forming neat straight lines, which ran the length of the playground. Each child stood exactly a foot behind the one in front. Each line was exactly three feet from the one next to it.'
>
> 'All pupils shall obey the prefects,' chanted Rose, in the same stiff voice. 'The prefects are the voice of the Head-master'.

As in Soviet Russia during the cold war, and in East Berlin behind the wall, there is a pervasive undercurrent of fear. Individual children suspect that they are being watched — and they are reluctant to speak their own thoughts, and soon become incapable of doing so. They are also scared that what they say may be mis-represented, or wrongly reported.

Dinah, the bright schoolgirl in *The Demon Headmaster*, is talking with Lucy, a younger pupil.

'Have you been at the school a long time?' she murmured.

'Since I was five,' Lucy whispered. ' Ssh! We're not supposed to talk.' She looked nervously over her shoulder.

'There's no one there, Dinah said encouragingly. We're the last. Do you like the school?

She had half expected the answer, but it was still a shock when she heard it. Lucy turned to look at her and said in a rather mechanical voice, 'The Headmaster is a marvellous man, and this is the best school I've ever been to'.

In fact, it was the only school Lucy had been to but this contradiction did not puncture the brainwashed opinions. Her hypnotically induced statements and her true beliefs co-existed like the doublethink of George Orwell's *Nineteen-Eighty-Four*.

The headmaster in Gillian Cross's stories hypnotised people purely with his eyes, and could do so even through a television camera. But this notion is not limited to children's' fiction. *Holy Smoke*, a feature film directed by Jane Campion, is a study about a cult. Initially set in India, two middle-class Western women travelling together have been attending the gatherings of a religious group.   The teacher of the group is administering 'darshan' a traditional practice in several faiths in which the 'leader' allows his gaze to pass at brow level over the 'third' eye of each of the people gathered.   I have personally experienced darshan at meditation meetings of the Brahma Kumaris, one of the spiritual movements to have come out of India in recent years. A seasoned meditator within the spiritual organisation will give the gift of darshan to the entire gathering. This can be a loving and a melting experience. It can move the receiver to tears.

In the film, the leader of the group is described as a guru, and he has penetrating, piercing, luminescent green eyes. Ruth (played by Kate Winslett), as she receives darshan, is moved beyond normal consciousness. The spiritual shift is so profound that she resolves to remain whilst her friend returns home to the West. Reporting back to Ruth's parents, her friend's version of events is:

> "It was so scary. Some sort of freaky hypnotism happened. I think they were on drugs. She even burned her airline ticket in front of me".

Hypnotism and drugs ... a potent cocktail! And yet, neither hypnosis nor drugs is evident in the religious group featured in *Holy Smoke*. The only high is the spiritual high that is accessed through meditation and Ruth's openness to receiving darshan.   The film ambivalently leaves open the question of whether Ruth freely remained in India as a reasonable response to her discovery of something that was — to her — of massive personal significance; or whether she was coerced by some mysterious and unstoppable force exerted by the guru. Nevertheless, the film does propagate the notion of 'hypnosis' as an intangible form of coercion that is exerted through the eyes.

Despite Ruth's insistence that she is staying voluntarily, her family bring in a 'cult exiter', a sort of modern-day exorcist, played by Harvey Keitel.

> "The mind is a mystery. I steer the subject through a breakdown situation. One: isolate; get her attention; win her respect. When she is resisting, I start to push her. It is very traumatic, which it is meant to be. Two: remove all her props. Three: finally, the clouds of her unreason break open. Tears, sobs, and it is over."

Cults use coercive and deceptive methods to capture the body and the mind. The cult exiter uses coercive and deceptive methods to recapture them. "One fire drives out one fire. One nail, one nail", as Shakespeare wrote in Coriolanus.

Yet, this is nothing like how interactive hypnotherapy works. Quite the opposite, in fact. Hypnosis is never a state that is imposed against a client's will, or slipped into without the client's knowledge. In interactive hypnotherapy, the therapist is like a tour guide accompanying you into the temple of your own mind, guiding you towards the insights and helping you harness the inherent powers that belong to you. *You* are steering.

The artist David Hockney took his inspiration for the painting featured on the cover of this book, from a scene in the movie, *The Raven*. Hockney's *The Hypnotist* (painted in 1963) is besuited in black, 'zapping' a dazzled, disarmed, on-stage subject dressed in a long scarlet robe, a robe that envelops arms, hands and feet. Both are depicted as theatrical beings. Their stage presence is further defined by turquoise drapes framing the scene. A crystal ball separates the broad space that separates the two figures. This crystal ball is positioned at floor level, slightly closer to the hypnotist, adding to the sense of mystery and sense of the maverick in both hypnotist and creator. When I saw Hockney's *The Hypnotist* at the Whitechapel Art Gallery, the painting was also featured in a commemorative video made by school children. Two teenage school friends had been captured on the video standing alongside the painting — caught on camera re-enacting the 'drama', one girl pretending to hypnotise the other. Mere moments of mimicry, reinforcing the myth.

A recent commercial for a canned drink embraces many of the same ingredients of the loss-of-control legend of hypnosis. The scene for the advertisement is set in a hypnotherapist's office. The client, a professional woman, is reclining on the ubiquitous leather couch, eyes closed. Relaxed. The poised, elegant fingertips of the hypnotherapist are touching. There is a soupçon of suspicion. The stage is set.

Now you're going deeper, and deeper. Now when I click my fingers you will sit up, and give me your Irn-Bru.

Click of fingers. The passive and obedient client sits up compliantly, reaches over, picks up, and hands over the can of drink. The hypnotherapist takes it and is seen savouring the Irn-Bru. Then, with deliberate indifference and irreverence he turns to the client and says, "Oh, but you're still a goat." The professional female falls on all fours braying — like a goat. The advertisement cuts to her tugging with her teeth at a pair of male underpants hanging on a washing line.

The advertisement is undoubtedly memorable in more ways than seeding the desirability of the drink. The notion that you can get the drink in any number of creative and inventive ways was central to the Irn-Bru campaign. This particular advertisement illustrates many of the tenets that also feature in the constant subtext of the staged hypnotist. The professional appears to inform the viewer that, if she should ever see a hypnotherapist, she will be under the control of the hypnotist, and that she will follow his instructions to the letter.

When I asked Gillian Cross, author of *The Demon Head-master*, about the source of her portrayal of hypnosis by eye-power, she responded by saying that, "Children find the books funny as well as exciting. They know that they are not to be taken seriously. In particular, children understand that the Head-master's hypnotic powers belong to the world of fantasy and magic, and not the real world". Her strong impression is that children and teachers already understand this very well. It is a view that has probably been shared by many other writers, from Rudyard Kipling onwards. Certainly, *if* a child were aware of the truth about a certain thing, then she can tell the difference between truth and fantasy. But very few people and especially few children actually do have a factually correct picture of what is involved in hypnosis, let alone hypnotherapy. Whereas encountering other professionals — such as, say, going to the doctor, the dentist, or the hairdresser — is part of the mundane world of almost all children in the west, going to the hypnotherapist is not. So they have no objective reference with which to compare the demon headmaster's methods. Moreover, they are given a fairly uniform picture across many different media: books, films, and advertising. All these sources portray hypnosis as having these salient characteristics:

- ◎ The hypnotist does the hypnotising by beaming some mysterious power from her eyes. Or the hypnotist does it by swinging some enigmatically potent pendulum in front of the subject's eyes.

- ◎ Hypnosis is an involuntary state, in which the hypnotist's will overpowers the victim's mind.

- ◎ Only the victim's strength of will can repel the hypnotist's power. Hence only weak-willed people can be hypnotised.

- ◎ While you are under hypnosis, the hypnotist has unlimited control over you: she can force you to tell her anything you know (even things that you did not consciously remember), and she can make you do anything during hypnosis, and she can force you to do anything afterwards.

◎   While you are hypnotised, you do not know that you are hypnotised, and you have no conscious awareness of what is going on.

◎   After you have come out of hypnosis, you will remember nothing of what happened, not even the fact that you were hypnotised.

Every one of these characteristics is wrong. The truth is the precise opposite in each case. Yet, this is the only picture of hypnosis being fed to young people, and it is being fed to them persistently and consistently from many different, trusted sources. Not surprisingly, this is the picture that they absorb and carry with them for the rest of their lives. And this is precisely the picture that I find, time and time again, still present in grown-ups, making them wary about hypnotherapy. A typical conversation at a party might include this exchange:

"What do you do for a living, Deborah?"

"I'm a hypnotherapist."

"I could never be hypnotised."

"Really? How did you come to think that?"

"I couldn't bear the thought of losing control. I couldn't just hand over control of my mind to someone else. I don't know what I might say. I might spill out all my secret thoughts. Anyway, I don't think I could be hypnotised, I'm too strong willed."

"And where did you get these ideas about hypnosis?"

"Oh, I don't know. Common knowledge, I suppose! From

the television, and I saw a guy perform at the university when I was studying. You wouldn't get me doing stuff like that!"

A taxi driver, driving me to a hypnosis conference in the coastal resort of Scarborough quipped:

"Just don't look into my eyes! My mate saw one of you lot, and — to this day — he's still working as a donkey on the beach in Robin Hood's Bay."

Well, I also thought it was funny at the time too.

Needless to say, the jokes and the mistaken 'common knowledge' do not spring out of thin air. They come from sources that are actually quite visible. But, as always, we have to open our eyes to see them.

Stage hypnotists play up to, and reinforce, the mistaken conception of hypnosis that most people will already have acquired through other media. Even if you've never seen a stage hypnosis act, you will have heard outline descriptions of it from friends, or read about it in reviews in magazines and newspapers, or seen references to it in sitcoms on television. Several of the fantasy features of hypnosis that I listed above may well be part of stage shows. One big difference is that stage hypnotists do not simply use their eyes to hypnotise. At most, the eyes may be used as a convenient focus for the subject to focus his gaze, but they do not emit hypnotic power.

In fact, a stage hypnotist is rather interested in the eyes of the audience. Jerry Valley, an American stage hypnotist, instructs students of stage hypnosis to "Watch your subjects. You can tell when a person is really paying attention by a certain fixation of their gaze." Early on in the performance a range of 'tests' will guide the hypnotist to recognise fixed gazes and behaviours, such as being unable to release their fingers following the finger-lock test. This lets the hypnotist find those members of the audience who are susceptible to hypnosis. From that group, he will select certain subjects for the show who are going to be easily and effortlessly suggestible to theatrical direction. Those are the ones to become entertainment fodder. The stage hypnotist's agenda centres on setting up dramatic scenarios with willing and submissive subjects.

By contrast, a hypnotherapist will work with everyone, not just a selected handful, not just a handful of the easiest and most malleable.

The hypnotised subjects whom you may have seen on television have been hypnotised off camera. When the cameras start to roll, the participants are in a state of so-called 'waking hypnosis'. A post-hypnotic suggestion has been given to the effect that the subjects will fall swiftly and easily into a relaxed state on receiving some trigger gesture. This can be the click of the hypnotist's fingers, or a movement of the hand in front of the subject's eyes. This produces an illusion for the television viewers that the hypnotist has the power to induce hypnosis swiftly through a mysteriously powerful, though seemingly mundane gesture. This is wonderful for dramatic effect and televisual appeal.

An hypnotic induction will never be shown on television, to avoid running the risk of hypnotising the viewing public. Like a magician, a stage hypnotist is trained in the art of illusion and showmanship. There is an element of 'trickery' and, in a different sense, sleight of hand.

That people are in the audience of a hypnotic show, and have volunteered to take part, may suggest that some are already some way toward going along with much that the hypnotist instructs. But alas not always. Stage shows sometimes do go very wrong. Take the case of regression and childhood. Interactive hypnotherapy can take you to specific influencing events and experiences in any particular year of your adolescence and childhood. You can go back to when you were eight years of age and were the subject of physical or verbal abuse — as did a woman in a stage show in Bolton in 1994. Age regression in stage hypnotism was, in fact, banned by a Home Office circular in 1989. This particular hypnotist got around the ban by telling the subject to imagine she was *a* child of eight, rather than explicitly taking her back to her *own* childhood aged eight. The subtlety of this legal loophole was lost on the woman's subconscious, which threw her into a re-experiencing of childhood sexual abuse. Amazingly, this loophole was left open by a further Home Office circular in 1996. The Home Office currently prohibits stage hypnosis that involves age regression, the suggested loss of body parts or the consumption of noxious substances, the blocking of pain inflicted by the hypnotist, and any demonstration in which the subject is suspended between supports (and in which hypnotists have been known to walk on the suspended subject!). Needless to say, imaginative stage hypnotists will find plenty of other ways to abuse the subject. For example, the Home Office circular does not prohibit the suggestion that the subject is being electrocuted. This is despite the fact that, in 1993, a young woman died after taking part in a stage show in Leyland, in which the hypnotist gave the suggestion of 10,000 volts of electricity passing through her. The coroner recorded death by natural causes, but the case led to the formation of the Campaign Against Stage Hypnosis by the young woman's mother, Margaret Harper. (See the research paper by Dr O'Keefe).

After five years, the Bolton case was won by the woman. This case highlighted the danger and irresponsibility of regression hypnosis on stage. In the case concerned, the stage hypnotist had persisted with his act, even though the subject conveyed her distress both verbally and physically. The subject was mere entertainment fodder. He persisted to convey the impression that he was making the subject do his bidding, ignoring her obvious resistance, and her tears. The court ruled that the subject had incurred significant emotional distress as a result of the stage experience and she was awarded compensation. (See news reports by the BBC and David Graves.)

When the Home Office reviewed the workings of the 1952 Hypnosis Act in 1996, they focused on specific harm done to individuals by stage hypnotists — such as "distress and anxiety" and "headaches and dizziness". Their remit did not include the adverse impact that stage hypnosis has on the public understanding of hypnotherapy. They noted that "thousands of people participate actively in stage hypnosis shows each year, and many thousands more attend", but they did not ask whether this might lead to widespread disinformation about therapeutic hypnosis. They also noted that "the hypnotist represents an authority figure whom the subject is asked to trust and obey. Many subjects have expectations of the power of hypnosis and their own subsequent *loss of control*. Under stage hypnosis the hypnotist will often further *encourage this belief*" (my emphasis). But they did not ask how many people are deterred from considering valuable hypnotherapy by such mistaken beliefs.

The universal myths associated with hypnotists are not going away, and creators of fiction are entitled to concoct whatever notions they wish. It is *caveat emptor* for the readers of their works to differentiate myth from realism. Correspondingly, it is a job for the hypnotherapeutic professionals to combat this widespread misunderstanding — which is the main reason that I wrote this book. That there is a single, standard, mythical picture of hypnosis is confirmed time and again. In one of the episodes of the British television reality show *Big Brother* in 2002, the televised participants undertook a 'task' involving hypnosis for fun, again complying perfectly with the popular conception of hypnosis as entertainment. This display amongst a group of 'housemates', who were most definitely up to be entertainment fodder, provided another example of a media circus. These kinds of 'dumbed down' scenarios contribute further to the debasement of hypnotherapy. They detract from the potential of hypnosis when more constructive purposes are kept in mind.

The biggest single misconception of this picture is that you are passive when undergoing hypnotherapy. Not so! As Michael Nash, writing for Scientific American wrote:

> "Under hypnosis subjects do not behave as passive automatons but instead are active problem solvers who incorporate their moral and cultural ideas."

The second biggest misconception is that hypnotic suggestions can arbitrarily override your own desires, your values, and your natural inclinations. In fact, if any form of words or ideas were to be introduced during your hypnotherapy that were contrary to your morals, your values, beliefs, or culture — that defied them, be they matters of faith or otherwise — then you would very likely open your eyes, effectively leaving the trance state. Alternatively you will ignore or compensate for the suggestion. As illustration of this, I recently invited the 'wise being' chosen by a client to hug the client and to tell the client how much he loved him, and further, how special the client grows up to be. In conversation at the end of the session, Joe said, "I couldn't really do that. My wise being was an older mate, and though we do love each other, it's unspoken. We wouldn't say it." In other words, you will not do anything that is in any way contrary to the behaviours you would be pre-disposed to do in full conscious awareness. In the Irn-Bru advertisement, the client is meeting an instruction that is not contrary to her normal behaviour. She feels comfortable in handing over the drink. The pretence of being a goat, however, borrows directly from stage scenarios. In the hypnotist's act, a member of the audience is chosen to go onto the stage to function as entertainment fodder. The volunteer will be asked to act out scenes and scenarios as instructed by the stage hypnotist, but only within certain limits. This performance on stage will continue only as long as the volunteer is comfortable with it. If the hypnotist should instruct the volunteer to do something outside his range of socially acceptable behaviour, he will snap out of the trance.

To be sure, there are instances of rogue hypnotherapists, who abuse the trust that clients place in them. Nevertheless, their abuse is not specifically mediated by hypnosis. It is rather a result of someone taking advantage of a natural tendency of the majority of people 'to please' and to obey figures of authority

Stanley Milgram conducted a classic series of psychological experiments in 1961-62 at Yale University, which demonstrated the degree of power wielded simply by someone playing the role of an authority figure. In this experiment, the apparatus consisted of an electric chair that administered electric shocks, and a control panel that could be used to apply graded shocks, apparently from

14 volts to 450 volts. A subject (the 'learner') was strapped in, with the electrode on his skin. A second participant (the 'teacher') was seated at the control panel. The experimenter stood by and instructed the 'teacher' when to start the experiment and when she could stop. In fact, the electric chair was a fake and could not produce anything more than a harmless 45-volt shock. Furthermore, the 'learner' was an actor who pretended to receive the increasingly higher shocks up to 450 volts. The 'teacher', however, did not know the chair was a fake, or that the 'learner' was acting. As far as the 'teacher' was concerned, the electric chair was real, as were the 'learner's' responses to the shocks. In the experimental procedure, the 'learner' had to memorise lists of words, and the 'teacher' had to apply a punishment in the form of an electric shock whenever the learner got one wrong. The surprising and dismaying result of this experiment was that the majority of the volunteers who played the role of 'teacher' were willing to inflict what they believed to be intensely painful, dangerous, or even lethal, electric shocks to the person in the 'learner' role. Subjects who were playing the 'teacher' role were never hypnotised, nor were they promised any reward for carrying on with the experiment nor threatened with any penalty for refusing. It was purely the aura of authority that led most of them to behave in a manner that they knew to be morally wrong. In a variant of the basic experiment, Dr Milgram placed the experimenter in another building, communicating by telephone. In that case, most of the 'teachers' refused to inflict dangerous shocks. The physical

presence of the experimenter was necessary for the aura of authority to be effective.

In those rare cases where rogue hypnotherapists have abused a client, possibly even assaulting the client, the key element is the hypnotist's role of authority. The fact that the client was placed in a relaxed and receptive state may have exacerbated the situation, but it is not the case that the hypnosis was an instrument of control.

In Stanley Milgram's experiments, it is clear from the transcripts that the subjects playing the role of 'teacher' were not relaxed but highly distressed by what they were being compelled by authority to do. Any significant clash of values will likewise bring a hypnotised person out of the relaxed state of trance and bring the full conscious attention to bear on the matter. The problem, then, is not the abuse of hypnosis but the abuse of trust.

Many people who would benefit from hypnotherapy nevertheless avoid it because they do not wish to have their mind 'messed with'. Yet, if by 'mind messing' we mean surreptitious influences on our thoughts, then in fact anyone who lives in a city or is exposed to modern media such as television and newspapers, is already being subjected to subliminal mind messing on a daily basis. The constant battery of commercial advertising, and the ideological biases of news media, are constantly trickling in through the gaps in our attention.

The human mind is remarkably susceptible to subtle suggestions all the time, and you do not need hypnosis to be influenced by them. This notion that your beliefs and thoughts may be influenced by suggestions that you were not even aware of may take some getting used to though. Surprise about this may lead people to doubt that it even takes place. John Lilly, in his book, *The Center of the Cyclone* (1972), describes an experiment where volunteers were influenced by words that were shown to them at the very edge of their peripheral vision, where they could not consciously read the words:

> We noticed that some subjects were quite upset with these effects, which were beyond their immediate conscious control. They would not accept the fact that their brain was reading a word and registering the meaning of that word below their levels of awareness. No matter how hard they tried they could not read the word ...

Needless to say, such research results come as no surprise to advertisers!

So far, we have been looking at how hypnosis is seen in the popular media. We will now turn to the medical profession and look at how hypnosis is regarded in that discipline. Here, we might hope to find a more perceptive understanding of the technique. Sadly, we are disappointed. At the start of the twentieth century, Dr Sigmund Freud (1859-1939) did a great disservice to the nascent field of hypnotherapy, by abandoning hypnosis as a therapeutic tool for reasons that had more to do with his lack of competence in the technique than with the efficacy of the technique itself.

The use of hypnosis in treating hysteria had been pioneered by the French doctors Jean Charcot (1825-1893) and Hippolyte Bernheim (1837-1919). Freud acquired the technique when he attended the charismatic Charcot's lectures in Paris in 1885, and he then experimented with Bernheim's style of hypnotherapy, which was simply the direct suggestion of symptom removal. He then turned to the cathartic hypnotherapy of Breuer, before dropping hypnosis completely in favour of his psychoanalytic techniques such as free association. Ray Udolf, in his *Handbook of Hypnosis for Professionals*, summarises Freud's reasons for subsequently abandoning hypnosis under the following six headings. We will go through these in some detail, because of the enormous influence Freud has had on psychotherapeutic practice over the past century.

(1)   Not everyone could be hypnotised

Freud found that individuals differed in how susceptible they were to being brought into the hypnotic state. This did not fit in with Freud's idealistic hope that psychotherapy should be wholly predictable. He had taken surgery as a role model for psychotherapy, and expected a treatment for hysteria to be as dependable as treating a broken leg. Even in Freud's hands, hypnosis had proven to be very effective for some patients, but this promising partial success was sacrificed to his belief that psychotherapy had to be a mechanistic process of unblocking 'psychic energy' with uniform results.

Most people can be hypnotised, and the limited success rate of Freud's hypnotic induction suggests that he had simply not developed an adequate technique. A widely respected early study at the University of Wisconsin found that only 9% of subjects were classed as 'non-hypnotisable' (Lawrence Davis and Richard Husband, 1931). The precise numbers will depend on which test of 'hypnotisability' is used, and on the demographic make-up of the subjects who are chosen for the test. Nevertheless, a similar proportion is generally accepted in hypnotherapeutic circles. In his early hypnotherapeutic practice, Dr J.M. Bramwell (*Hypnotism*, 1928) found that between 80% and 97% were capable of some degree of hypnotic response; later research by LeCron and Bordeaux (*Hypnotism Today*, 1947) found that 85% to 90% could enter at least a light trance. In my own work, I have found that only about 5% of clients cannot be taken into useful depth of hypnosis in the first session. I have also found that susceptibility to hypnosis increases in successive sessions. Clients who do not enter a usable hypnotic state in the first session often do so in the second session. This agrees with early findings reported by Kuhn & Rosso, in *Modern Hypnosis* (1947): Failure to achieve hypnosis may be due to lack of persistence. Hypnotists often try only a few times. There are cases of success after twenty failures. In one instance a man was hypnotised after 700 consecutive failures.

(2)   Patients needed to re-experience recovered memories

When a patient had recovered a memory of some painful event that was causing the neurosis, Freud found that he would then have to get the patient to re-experience the remembered event. This meant that the actual therapeutic work had to be done after the hypnotic work, which obviously diminished the value of the hypnotic part of the process.

In fact, it is perfectly possible for a subject to re-experience a trauma in hypnosis, and to remember fully what happened after leaving the hypnotic state. Again, Freud's failure to get his patients to do this suggests a deficiency in his competence.

Nevertheless, interactive hypnotherapy does not actually involve re-experiencing the full emotional blast of an event, a situation, or a circumstance in a person's life. Instead, interactive hypnotherapy can handle the disruptive factor symbolically and transmute and neutralise it in that way alone.

By contrast, Freud's method relied on bringing the recovered memory fully into consciousness on the assumption that the conscious mind will then be able to rationalise it, and dissipate its disruptive power. That may happen over time, but it can be slow and haphazard.

(3)   Hypnosis took away patients' 'defences' too quickly

Part of the Freud's thinking was that patients had to lower their mental defences in a gradual and systematic way. Whilst this may be true in the comparatively uncontrolled process of psycho-analysis, it is not true in the more controlled process of interactive hypnotherapy. The defence mechanisms can safely be dropped because the hypnotherapist will be guiding the subject every step of the way. The client is not left to confront recovered traumas defencelessly: the hypnotherapist takes the client in hand and leads him through the process of reconciling, and gaining power over, whatever is uncovered during hypnosis. Moreover, the client at younger ages in the process, is supported, protected and strengthened by their older self, and a wise-being or mentor whom they themselves have chosen to be by their side.

(4)   Hypnosis did not produce a permanent cure

Freud claimed that hypnosis produced only a transient cure. This again suggests that his technique may not have been adequately developed. He believed that merely re-experiencing past events was sufficient to effect a cure. In fact, this is true only in a minority of cases. In the majority of cases, the client must actively negotiate the dissolution, or transformation, of whatever is causing the problem. In failing to help his client's find fresh ingredients for growth and change, Freud left the disturbing influence intact and potentially still active, albeit temporarily unattached.

We may think of Freudian analysis as tilling the soil, and leaving the roots lying on the surface, in the hope they would shrivel and die in the sun. With no active 'weed-killer', so to speak, weeds tend to re-root, to re-establish, and to grow back again. In contrast, interactive hypnotherapy — having up-rooted the negative emotions, guides you through a process of either destroying and eliminating those roots or transforming them into something beneficial.

(5)   Hypnosis took too long

Freud claimed that hypnotherapy took too long to achieve its results. This is a surprising claim, in view of the extraordinary lengths of time that Freudian psychoanalysis was to take up. Speigel and Speigel vividly summarise the mammoth scale of a psychoanalytic treatment (*Trance and Treatment*, 1978):

> When Freud first developed psychoanalysis, the average course of treatment was approximately six months. One stopped what one was doing and journeyed to Vienna to be analysed by the master. In view of the time involved, it was not terribly unreasonable for Freud to ask the patient not to make any major life decisions, to avoid the acting out of transference material. Analysts currently view such analyses as incomplete, and the treatment has expanded to a course of three to five years. Kleinian analyses can go on for eight years or more.

In contrast, a typical course of interactive hypnotherapy takes three to five sessions to achieve what is usually a permanent result. Any subsequent backsliding from the result may be reversed by a top-up session. The methods of modern interactive hypnotherapy are driven by results rather than ideology. Freud's starting point was his abstract model of the unconscious mind, and his therapeutic practice was forced into that mould. The interactive hypnotherapist's starting point is the commitment to address, and to resolve, a specific problem in the client's life, and the therapeutic practice is structured to achieve that single result as quickly as possible.

(6)   Hypnosis is too sexual

The final objection that Freud raised to the therapeutic use of hypnosis was both the strangest and, for him, the most definitive. It concerns the common psychotherapeutic phenomenon of 'transference'. Anthony Storr wrote (*Solitude, A Return to the Self*):

> Today psychoanalysis now insists that analysis of transference, that is, of the patient's emotional response to, and attitude toward, the psychoanalyst is the most essential feature of psychoanalytic treatment.

Freud, however, was troubled by this dynamic when he first encountered it in hypnotherapy:

> He saw his own role as that of a detached observer, and assumed that his patients would have the same attitude towards him as they would toward a medical specialist in any other field.

Freud wrote as late as 1910, in a letter to Oskar Pfister:

> As for the transference, it is altogether a curse. The intractable and fierce impulses in the illness, on account of which I renounced both indirect and hypnotic suggestion...

It is not just the occurrence of transference during hypnotherapy that bothered Freud, for in fact transference is an unavoidable part of psychoanalysis too. What bothered him was that it seemed to play an uncontrollable central role in hypnosis. This emerges when Freud expands on his reasons for giving up hypnosis (Freud, 1935, quoted by Spiegel & Speigel, 1978):

> And one day I had an experience which showed me in the crudest light what I have long suspected. One of my most acquiescing patients, with whom hypnotism had enabled me to bring about the most marvellous results, and whom I was engaged in relieving of her suffering by tracing back her attacks of pain to their origins, as she woke up on one occasion, threw her arms round my neck. The unexpected entrance of a servant relieved us from the discussion. From that time onwards there was a tacit understanding between us that the hypnotic treatment should be discontinued. I was modest enough not to attribute the event to my own irresistible personal attractions, and I felt that I had now grasped the nature of the mysterious element that was at work behind hypnotism. In order to exclude it, or at all events to isolate it, it was necessary to abandon hypnotism.

Kuhn & Rosso, in *Modern Hypnosis* (1947) were more explicit about Freud's bizarre misconception of hypnosis:

> "Freud compares hypnosis to being in love. In hypnosis he found the same compliance, subjection, and absence of critical faculty found in lovers. The hypnotiser takes the

role of the beloved one and the rapport between the hypnotiser and the hypnotised is an erotic tie. Hence hypnosis is an artificial form of love without any sexual satisfaction included."

Freud's weird notion of hypnosis as romantic reverie was objectively demolished by the research of Davis and Husband, which reported in 1931 that there was no correlation whatsoever between hypnotisability and sexuality.

Despite his high regard as an innovator, it is widely recognised that Freud did not use hypnotherapy very effectively. Largely, this can be attributed to Freud's being driven by his theoretical assumptions, rather than allowing himself to be guided by the patient's own vocabulary. Dr Thierry Melchior wrote (in *The Milton H. Erickson Foundation Newsletter*, 1999):

In Studies on Hysteria and other papers of this period (1890-1897), Freud clearly states that if the patient doesn't recall what the doctor is prepared to discover (i.e., a sexual abuse), he has to say very firmly to the patient "You are wrong, this has nothing to do with what we are searching for, it is something else that has happened, continue to try to remember!" As a result, patients either fled away or ended up "remembering" the abuse. Those who ended in "remembering" were probably highly motivated to do so, first because of Freud's intense pressure, and second, because Freud has led them to believe that remembering was the only way to get rid of their painful symptoms, whatever they were.

This is the exact opposite of the working method of modern interactive hypnotherapy, where the therapist accepts and uses precisely the words and the phrases and the sentences the client speaks.

Were one to add a third substantive reason, it may well be Freud's considerable and over-bearing authority in the analytical arena.

As a practising hypnotherapist, I often find that clients come for hypnotherapy sessions after undergoing psychiatric help for some time. I always get to know about the psychiatrist whom my client is seeing. This information may be a part of our initial discussion or it may emerge as a consequence of my enquiring as to whether the client is taking any medication. In contrast, the psychiatrist rarely gets to know of the hypnotherapist that his patient is seeing. The reasons given by my client for keeping the hypnotherapy sessions secret often have to do with not wanting to do anything to upset the consultant, and particularly with wanting to avoid seeming to question the authority and medicinal diktat of the psychiatrist overseeing the case.

Dr Freud's damaging but ill-founded attack on hypnosis was only the first of many put-downs by the medical establishment.

We've seen what the media and the medical establishment have to say about hypnosis, but what about the hypnotherapists themselves? If we scan through the advertising literature of hypnotherapists, we find that it is predominantly 'legal, honest, and decent' (as the UK Advertising Standards Authority neatly summarises the criteria for acceptable advertising). Sadly, a few hypnotherapists are not quite as scrupulous as we might like.

The first test is whether the promotional literature seeks to empower you, the client, or the hypnotherapist. Bear in mind that hypnotherapy is about putting *you* in the driving seat, not the therapist. I recently came across the following copy-line in a hypnotherapist's advertisement: "I am honoured to facilitate your wellness," which I think strikes the right balance between client and therapist.

One of the ways in which a few hypnotherapists like to make themselves look important is by tagging strings of mysterious letters and titles after their names. For example, you will occasionally see advertisements for a 'Registered Hypnotherapist'. That sounds reassuringly impressive, but what precisely does it mean? How does one become a Registered Hypnotherapist in the UK? There are three essential steps. Step 1. Take a sheet of paper and a ballpoint pen. Step 2. At the top, write "Register". Step 3. Underneath, write your own name. You are now legally entitled to describe yourself as a Registered Hypnotherapist. In other words, in the UK at the present time, the phrase on its own means very little. You always have to ask, *whose* register? Needless to say, the majority of responsible hypnotherapists are disenchanted by the cavalier use of terms such as "registered". This highlights a blind spots of the Advertising Standards Agency, who have no guidelines for the use of the word "registered", so there is no penalty for those who misuse this term.

Promotional literature that quotes a string of letters after the hypnotherapist's name should always spell out what the letters mean if they are not in common usage. You, the prospective client, can then look up the relevant organisation, to judge the significance of the quoted letters. On my own web site, for instance, I quote "FHS (Emeritus)" and "FRSH" and in the same paragraph I state that these mean "Emeritus Fellow of the Hypnotherapy Society" and "Fellow of the Royal Society for the Promotion of Health". These are both well-established highly professional bodies that have their own web sites, where interested readers can find out more information.

In scanning advertisements for hypnotherapy, the strings of letters you will come across, fall into certain groups within the alphabet soup of accreditations. First, you will see the common academic qualifications. The BA ('Bachelor of Arts') and the BSc ('Bachelor of Science') are first degrees, obtained by three or four years' study; the MA ('Master of Arts') and the MSc ('Master of Science') are higher degrees, obtained by advanced study or research. The PhD, or DPhil in Oxford ('Doctor of Philosophy') is obtained by three or more years of research and qualifies the person as a 'doctor', but not of medicine. The MD ('Doctor of Medicine') is the qualification of the standard medical doctor. These qualifications are for life. Second, there are memberships of professional bodies, such as FHS ('Fellow of the Hypnotherapy Society') and MHS (Member of the Hypnotherapy Society). Being a Fellow involves meeting professional standards and the membership can be revoked if a practitioner fails to keep up those standards. An 'Emeritus Fellow' (sometimes indicated by "Em" in front of the letters) has been recognised as having made an especial contribution to the field. A hypnotherapist may well be a Fellow or a Member of several bodies, including ones not directly connected to hypnotherapy. For example, an FCPS is a Fellow of the College of Physicians and Surgeons, and an FRGS is a Fellow of the Royal Geographical Society who may have carried out medical work abroad. Third, there are hypnotherapeutic qualifications. Here the alphabet soup gets quite dense. There are accreditations to do with clinical hypnotherapy, which is a fairly specific standard, as well as certificates awarded by numerous private schools that vary in their standards. It really is crucial for these to be explained in a therapist's promotional literature. To begin with, the letters must be spelt out. For example, is a DCH a Diploma or a Doctorate (in Clinical Hypnotherapy)? For clarity, a diploma should be indicated by 'Dip' rather than 'D' but it often is not. A diploma from a private hypnotherapy school should be written as DipHyp (ABC) where ABC indicates the school. With so much variability in hypnotherapeutic accreditations, you should look at independent reviews and testimonials for the individual hypnotherapist. In time, more rigorous and reliable standards will be recognised in this field, and the Hypnotherapy

Society in the UK is actively promoting this development. But it will take time.

Performing a search on the World Wide Web for 'Harley Street Hypnotherapy' will generate 1500 responses. Narrow this down to individual hypnotherapists, and you're in business. Big business, in fact. More than likely there are plenty more Harley Street Hypnotherapists than there are offices on a daily or hourly basis to administrate them all. Mention 'Harley Street' and most people would believe that they must be getting the best. In fact, the power of suggestive association just scored another few pounds. Yes, some of the most eminent doctors, surgeons, dentists and consultants have worked, and continue to work, out of offices in historic Harley Street. When it comes to hypnotherapy, though, it *can* be a front. 'Location. Location. Location' may be the bottom line for marketing property, but it is irrelevant when you are judging which hypnotherapists in your area would be best for you. Look behind the scenes. Look for professionalism with a heart. As any professional hypnotherapist will tell you, it takes much more than a commitment to pay premium rents. Of course, there *are* good hypnotherapists in Harley Street, but you cannot rely on that street address alone as proof of a therapist's quality.

In the UK, the Advertising Standards Authority (ASA) regulates advertising copy that appears in magazines and newspapers. The ASA's web site has a searchable list of past cases. If you run a search for the keywords "hypnosis" or "hypnotherapy" you get a list of misdemeanours in our area of interest. It makes for interesting reading. Listed below are some of the recent breaches of the ASA guidelines. These bring to your notice some things that you should be wary of when looking at the promotional literature of hypnotherapists. (If you wish to see the full list, complete with names, visit the ASA's web site. The reference is at the back of this book.)

Date	Advertiser's copy, and Authority's ruling
13/03/02	"Want to stop smoking? 1 session approx. 85% success rate" **Complaint upheld**: the Authority considered that, without a proper clinical study that supported the advertiser's methods and substantiated the claim, the claim was misleading.
06/02/02	"Dr ... D.C.H. (Doctor in Clinical Hypnotherapy)" **Complaint upheld:** The Authority considered the use of "Dr" implied that the advertiser was a medically qualified doctor and concluded that the advertisement was likely to mislead.
23/10/02	"[hypnotist] has helped over 5000 smokers to stop in one session ... 94% stop smoking with hypnotherapy" **Complaint upheld:** claims not substantiated.
10/01/02	"Advanced therapies — stop smoking in 1 hour 98% success rate." **Complaint upheld:** success rate not substantiated.
17/10/01	"Stop Smoking ... In just 2 sessions. Lifetime guarantee. Totally natural. 96% success rate." **Complain upheld:** success rate not substantiated.
11/07/01	"Stop smoking in 1 hour 95% success rate" **Complaint upheld:** success rate and number of sessions not substantiated.
09/05/01	"Tens of thousands of clients can't be wrong" in connection with a range of therapies including hypnotherapy **Complaint upheld:** claim not substantiated.
28/02/01	"I lost 105 lbs in ten months using hypnosis" **Complaint upheld:** claim not substantiated.
14/02/01	"The Center ... invites you to a free consultation with a choice of fully qualified hypnotherapists." **Complaint not upheld**: The Authority considered that, although no statutory body recognised the Institute of Clinical Hypnosis qualifications, most consumers would understand the advertisement to mean the hypnotherapists had completed a course in hypnotherapy and were sufficiently qualified to practise in that discipline.
12/04/99	"Smoker — Slim — Phobia — guarantee 90+ % success rate" **Complaint upheld**: success rate not substantiated.

If you see an advertisement for hypnotherapy that you think is misleading, then please do report it to the ASA, and they will investigate it. Do bear in mind, however, that the ASA's job is not to establish the efficacy and success rate of hypnosis, but to check whether advertisers have documentary evidence that substantiates the particular claims that they make. A blind spot of the ASA is, unfortunately, the whole of the internet. Their remit covers primarily printed media, such as newspapers, magazines, brochures, leaflets, circulars, mailings, fax transmissions, catalogues and follow-up literature. You could publish the most outrageous claims, flouting all of the ASA's guidelines, but if you do it only on a web site then the ASA cannot even investigate the case. So, please be especially wary when reading hypnotherapists' web sites!

As in other areas of consumer purchases, such as buying a domestic hi-fi, a robust approach is to read independent reviews and testimonials in order to help you assess what is on offer. Journalists are always keen to try out new things and report back to their readers, and therapists will normally keep a file of testimonials. You may ask to see them.

By now you may have gathered that I am tempted to get on my soapbox in Hyde Park Corner on Sunday morning and champion hypnotherapy with an evangelical swing! I believe in hypnotherapy. I am committed to making a contribution in some way to changing the public perception of hypnosis and hypnotherapy.

I was surprised when, last year, I applied for a merchant facility to take credit-card payments. I was politely informed by my bank, some considerable way into the application process, that hypnotherapy was one of the services that was on the list to be declined automatically. The reason, I discovered, was as follows. On occasions in the past, individuals had paid for a course of hypnotherapy that had been promoted in an advertisement that *guaranteed* the desired outcome, and they had paid for the sessions by credit card. Most frequently, the hypnotherapy in question had been to stop smoking. In the cases where the therapy to stop smoking had not succeeded, for whatever reason, the consumer, exercising the relevant legal right, was at liberty to claim the full cost of the sessions back from the credit-card company. Understandably the credit-card companies sought to avoid these situations. After some discussion – an education to both myself and my bank, my application was accepted on the proviso that card processing was not used to take payment for individual hypnotherapy sessions, but only for training courses and books. Surely a better and more convenient way forward would be to ban the word 'guarantee' from any advertisement for hypnotherapy services. Guarantees come with household appliances such as toasters. Guarantees do not come with hypnotherapy sessions. In fact, the Advertising Standards Agency does take a dim view of 'guaranteed' hypnotherapy results in printed advertisements, which is a good start!

So, let us sum up our conclusions from this chapter. As far as fiction is concerned:

◎   Don't believe a word you read in the stories!

As regards the medical establishment:

◎   The majority are not up-to-speed on the benefits of hypnotherapy.

And, as for the hypnotherapists' own promotional literature:

◎   Use common sense, and if in doubt ask for further information and justification. Bear in mind that hypnotherapeutic success is impossible to guarantee. Do not believe in 'guarantees' with respect to any complementary therapy!

◎   Check out the independent reviews.

◎   Check organisations and linking web sites.

4

◎

POSITIVELY ENTRANCED

Trances and trance-like states in everyday life

Trance has always been a mystery, and in many ways it remains so. Science today is not sure why hypnosis works, but the evidence that it does work stacks up. Trance is a natural way to achieve total stillness, a stillness that can be refreshing and satisfying in itself, and can even effect healing from within. Professor John Gruzelier's research under the auspices of Imperial College, London found that the mere experience of being in hypnosis, in a state of deep relaxation, with no direct suggestion or interactive participation whatsoever, could itself be beneficial and healing to patients. In particular, the research confirmed, that regular periods of deep relaxation increased the effectiveness of patients' medication and treatment

Compare and contrast this experience with the meditation practice prescribed by the Transcendental Meditation movement. Meditation 'is to be taken' twice daily for twenty minutes, morning and evening every day. As you will read again later in this chapter, I believe that hypnosis is a fast-track way to reach the same state that meditation brings. Practised meditators report that remembering to take time to minister to this prescription will facilitate mental balance, creativity, and a sense of well-being throughout the whole body and mind.

In the 1970s, John Lilly expressed the phenomena of trance in the apt terms of 'going with the flow', or 'letting go', as opposed to being 'up tight' (*Center of the Cyclone*, 1972):

> I did not particularly like the terminology of hypnosis because it implied something special, something removed from one's ordinary experience and something available only to professionals. In my own experience, these states are natural, simple, easy, obvious — once one is willing to go with the flow. ... If one is "up tight" and refuses to "let go" even though one would like to let go, these phenomena just do not occur as frequently.

It is likely that you have been positively entranced in one way or another already. If you have had one or more of the following experiences, then you will have already experienced a very light trance-like state to some level or degree. Trance-like inducers: cleaning your teeth; checking your mobile telephone for messages; playing computer games; performing a broad range of routine actions — all are performed semi-consciously or even non-consciously. We call these habits. There are good habits and there are not-so-good habits. Habits are actions and routines performed in a state of unconscious competence. They are performed in a state of light trance. Often, actions that start out as novelty assume very rapidly the nature of a habit.   Text messaging would be one recent example. Texting was a novelty at first — convenient and fast, but requiring some manual dexterity to enter long textual messages with just a numeric keypad. Now, for many, it is a habit — as easy and natural as speaking, it no longer requires conscious concentration on every key press. The paradigm of this automatism is touch-typing. An expert touch-typist transcends conscious awareness of keystrokes, and thinks only of the text. This migration from novelty, through conscious competence, to unconscious competence, is widespread. Taking drugs recreationally would be another — an ultimately much more disabling habit.

There are other common examples of trance. When you tie up your shoelaces you do so with unconscious competence. When you step into a lift in a department store you go into trance when you unconsciously turn around to face the door.   When you navigate through a city, either on foot or in a vehicle, while deep in thought or conversation, you are operating in a state of trance. Let us take a closer look at some particular forms of trance-like states: prayer, exercise, music, driving, yoga, massage, production lines and chatting on the telephone.

Prayer

Prayer can be a gateway into a mildly altered state of consciousness, in other words a mild trance — which can be relaxing, fulfilling, and healing. Statistical studies led by Larry

Dossey have confirmed anecdotal reports of the remedial effect of prayer.

People in prayer often close their eyes, and in so doing they enter a state different from when the eyes are open. With that gesture a person who prays moves by one small step from the outer world of the material to the inner world of the spirit.

Whoever is officiating at a service of faith will suggest to those gathered, "Let us pray!", and after some shuffling and adjustments to posture, people accept and action the command. Those gathered close their eyes and listen. They listen to the words of the given prayer, and they can also participate. Participatory words and phrases can almost sound like the words of an incantation. Groups gathered together for the purpose of worship often chant or repeat words of a holy and worshipful nature. Repetition induces a change in the person who says or hears them. Repetition brings about a sense of centring within the being in prayer, and naturally it provides a focus for the gathering. It narrows down the focus and the concentration, such that a person begins to experience a quietening within, and a peace within.

One positive prayerful experience leads to another. Devotees report that the repeated acts of prayer are 'character building'. Virtues, like patience are given an airing and plenty of opportunity to deepen and to grow. People who pray say that it is comforting and that it is relieving — relieving of emotions like guilt and worry. As a result people who pray feel increasingly calm after prayer and emerge from prayer, feeling they have done something good — something fulfilling. Such is the power of repetition, good intention, and action. A daily dose of prayer is, for many, a vital antidote to a soulless and pressurised modern world. In the City of London, home to a financial powerhouse of the globalised market place, we find that Sir Christopher Wren's ancient churches, large and small, attract a loyal band of individuals who pop in to the church on the way to work, to touch base with their inner selves and something beyond. Churches such as St Clements Eastcheap, for instance, have a vanishingly small congregation for formal services, but a large and growing following of people who value the special space and place in which they can hold on to their few minutes of spiritual engagement, in trance-like detachment from the day's hurly-burly.

Like hypnosis, prayer is not an out-of-mind state, prayer is an inner-mind state. With practice it fosters a relationship with oneself and with the divine. Hypnotherapy can be thought of as a kind of secular equivalent to prayer.

Interactive dialogues in hypnosis are often spoken entirely in whispers. A hypnotherapist may sit closely alongside you, because she needs to be able to hear what you say. A hypnotherapy session can be a prayerful experience. People often come to prayer as a last resort, too, so it seems that therapeutic hypnosis and prayer have even more in common. Perhaps both prayer and hypnotherapy are losing their unpopular image and are moving towards seeing more light of day, both being blessings in disguise. Like the experience of prayer, I liken the state of hypnosis to the state of meditation. Meditation may take longer to learn, but, like hypnosis, it is a tool that can throw light on what is going on at deeper levels of your thinking. Ultimately they are both practices that can bring a sense of clarity and understanding about mental processes, and hence freedom to experience oneself more fully and truthfully in the here and now.

Hypnosis, I would say, is a fast-track way to reach a meditative and contemplative state. Some may argue that different types of meditation involve carrying out quite different processes internally, but the experience of each is similar. In both you gain access to an encyclopaedia of inner wisdom. Reflective meditation requires that you speak respectfully with yourself. Often a sense of revelation, reconciliation, and a 'lightness of spirit' engages within you, having put all the negative thoughts to one side. You emerge as though you have deeply enjoyed a restful night's sleep. These meditative conversations can be compared to forms of prayer.

Exercise

Power walking, running on a treadmill, and pedalling vigorously on a stationary bicycle, all induce trance-like altered states of awareness. Joggers describe entering 'the zone', a different, high, and highly desirable state of consciousness. In these altered states you are potentially as responsive to hypnotic suggestions as you would be when hypnotised in a relaxed and therapeutic setting.

So it is that hypnosis can be induced during a programme of vigorous exercise.

During extended exercise such as running, your mind is released from its engagements with the daily cycle of work and responsibility. Your brain does not need to answer the phone, text a friend, check out a web site, or email a colleague. There is nothing to do but put one foot in front of the other. The whole mind can let go, and go with the flow. The rhythmic movement of steps locks the floating mind down to a stable state, accompanied by steady, deep breathing. The brain is in neutral — receptive and open. It is a mild trance state, which some people use to give themselves periods of enhanced creativity and a time to stand back and reflect on a bigger picture. Businessmen who use exercising trance in this way enthuse over how quickly they solve problems that seemed insoluble.

Music

Music is the food of love, as Shakespeare would have us believe. If so, it may be because the gods recognise how nutritious a supplement music is for spiritual fulfilment. While words may be food for thought, music is food for entrancing journeys into the inner mind. It may be said that music often bypasses the conscious mind.

Music takes us outside the realm of concepts and notions that can be defined and nailed down by words. To be sure, music can be emotionally evocative. It can make us happy or sad, brave or fearful, energetic or sleepy. But it can also take us into a realm of its own, a subtle state that is altered from our normal state in some inexpressible way. In that sometimes, sublime realm, we may find that we have access to inner mental resources of strength and creativity that are hard or impossible to reach otherwise.

Trance-like states induced by music share the characteristic of being able to reveal solutions to challenges that we face in life. They can show us the way to our hearts, to our true feelings about things. No longer weighed down and distracted by specifics and verbal straitjackets, music can give us hope, inspiration, and insight.

It is curious that amongst the current fashions of the music world there is now a genre called 'trance music'. To some extent, this is a product of the marketing chaps picking up on ideas that are in circulation, and creating a label and image to harness the interest that already exists. But it does also capture and bring to the fore the features of music that can help to induce mild trance. A lot of people, from students onwards, use music as a background stimulant whilst studying or working. It is I think, too dismissive to say that the music is a 'mental chewing gum'. Clearly, the music is being used in a mildly psychotropic way: to modify the state of the mind in certain specific ways — to focus it, to clear it, to illuminate it.

Driving

If you drive a car, then you enter into an altered state of relaxation on almost every trip you make. In that daydreaming state, you may come up with ideas for the home and for work. You may imagine decorating a room, writing a presentation, thinking up the menu for a social gathering, or endlessly re-playing more inspiring and witty responses to conversations you had hours, days, weeks, or years ago. On your brain's autopilot, you gain access to a deeper wisdom, and an ability to make connections that illuminate and inspire, and lead to future action. Some people do their best thinking in the car. The subconscious is very much to the fore, primarily observing the road, enabling you to travel in your mind far and away from your present situation. You manage to do this safely because your subconscious mind knows the route you are taking. You arrive at 'B' with no recollection of the drive from 'A'. Yet, you can come back to being fully aware of your surroundings in a heartbeat and apply the brake pedal with exquisite timing when you need to pull up quickly because the car in front of you is suddenly slowing down. In effect, you are driving in a trance-like state, in a state of light hypnosis. Yet, you are manifestly not asleep. Tragedies do occur when the driver falls asleep at the wheel and the brain ceases to be in control of the situation. In the relaxed but alert attentiveness of trance-like driving, the conscious mind may quietly slip into neutral, and drift onto a range of other topics, while the brain as a whole expertly retains control of the situation. This emphasises the complete difference between sleep and hypnosis.

Yoga

Another example is that of the relaxation experience at the end of a yoga class. The yoga teacher may direct you to relax from the top of your head to the tips of your toes, relaxing each and every part of your body progressively in turn. Although the end-result is very similar, the terminology is different. Although yoga would employ a different terminology, this experience is known to hypnotists as a progressive induction into a trance state.

Why is the progressive induction so effective? Telling someone to relax their whole body completely, in one go will not get very far, unless he or she is already trained in meditation or self-hypnosis. The multiplicity of different parts in the body, each with its own muscle groups — and each muscle group with its own tension, renders the body as a whole impossible to target for physical relaxation. Successful bodily relaxation relies on addressing individual parts separately. Rather than haphazardly picking out this and that part of the body, it is more effective to start at one end and work systematically through the whole frame of the body. That is because the skeletal muscles of the body form a balanced network: tension in one part triggers tension is neighbouring parts. I generally find starting with the toes and working up to the crown of the head is the better of the two possible directions. This is because higher-body tensions feed off the tensions lower down the body. There is nothing mystical about this: it is just that the mechanics of keeping the body upright against the pull of gravity requires that the lower muscle groups, in the legs and the spine, have a stronger role to play, and their tension influences the head and neck more than vice versa.

In yoga, each pose, or *asana*, performs a specific purpose. At the beginning and end of a yoga session, it is normal to finish off with the asana of complete relaxation, *savasana* (sometimes translated as the pose of the dead man). Outwardly, you are just lying down doing nothing. Inwardly, you are progressively relaxing every muscle group, then checking every part of the body for relaxation, and relaxing the nervous system, and finally disengaging the conscious mind from the room and everyday life in general. To those of you who have experienced this, I would say that you have experienced the trance state. You will have a pretty good notion of what it is like to experience hypnosis.

Massage

For some people, massage is the only route to reach the deep state of relaxation in which one is perfectly content to remain 'blissed out' without moving or fidgeting. It is not sleep, as the mind remains fully conscious and alert; nor is it temporary paralysis, for one could easily get up if one so desired. But it is a state from which one does not wish to be roused. This state is essentially the starting point for hypnotherapy, and is normally achieved by a spoken induction. A few per cent of people, however, find it hard to enter the deep relaxation through spoken induction, but some of them can nonetheless enter the same state through receiving massage.

Massage obviously bypasses the whole logical and linguistic apparatus that is generally under control of the conscious mind, especially in the left hemisphere of the brain. Massage at first relieves the physical tension of the skeletal muscles, but then with its reassuring and rhythmic motion it also allows the mind to let go of its tight grip on mundane life.

Production lines

People whose job is only to press a button or push a lever spend seven and a half hours a day in trance. Adhering to the necessarily repetitive actions and movements on a production line induces an altered state. Production lines function best with happy workers who wear the same uniform and who hold similar beliefs and values, and who can tune out. Amidst the background noise, conversation is negligible. Piped music aids and abets the lull. On a production line a person ceases to seek stimulation. Tuning out for longer and longer periods becomes a habit. Be it packing burgers, or pushing chocolates into line, the ease at which a line-worker can get into the altered state is perceived as a pre-requisite for the job.

Chatting on the telephone

Mobile phones are also masterful at inducing trance. You must have seen many times someone sitting using their telephone, perhaps a mobile phone in a crowded place, in a trance-like state oblivious of anyone else around. It is as though in some situations, people who use mobile phones in public places step into an invisible private room, a cocoon of their imagining. Speaking loudly, their conversations reiterate the frequently heard words and phrases: "I'm on a train..." "The train is just coming into the station. I'll be there in ten minutes". As this is a trance-like state that is induced as a by-product of something else, namely a remote conversation, it can tend to take on a life of its own, and eat into normal life.

> At the start of each session, I always ask, "Is your mobile phone switched off?" Recently, a client replied, in response to my question: "I've stopped using it. Yesterday was the changeover. It feels strange. My hope is, that I'll use a public phone box". She had decided to take control of a tool that felt like it had begun to control her. In the future will there be a trend to go back — towards more people making the resolve to walk, and to be mobile-free?

Charles Tart, in his comprehensive compilation, *Altered States*, maintains that what we call 'hypnosis' actually comprises three distinct sorts of altered state of consciousness. He also carefully differentiates between the altered states that are obtained in other situations, such as meditation. There is a lot of truth in this, and it would not suggest that all these different trance-like states amount to the same thing. The message that I want to get across is that trance-like states are mundane: they are part of normal, everyday life. For our purposes, the similarities between these trance-like states are more important than their differences.

In hypnotherapy, the trance state is the same kind of experience as the everyday light trances that we are familiar with. It differs only in being deeper, and that in a one to one hypnotherapy session the client is guided into the state. The therapist's words form an instruction, leading to a suggestion — towards relaxation.

> As I move my hand close, *close* your eyes, and as I move my hand past your nose and chin, take a deep breath and become beautifully, and deeply relaxed.

This instruction is part of a script devised by the American hypnotherapist David Elman. The technique is called simply 'The Closed Eye Process', and it is a technique I continue to favour for inducing hypnosis. This is just one of many equally valid inductions. I include it here at length, mainly to demystify the process. What I would like to do is dispel any seeds of doubt that Molly Moon may have planted in the back of your mind, that being hypnotised involves some invisible force acting upon you. You will be fully aware of everything that happens to you during the induction, and you will be freely and enjoyably drifting into a comfortable state of alert relaxation — a heightened state of relaxation.

THE ELMAN INDUCTION SCRIPT

"So, what I'd like you to do is to let your eyes
close. Begin to tune into the ebb and flow of
your breath — the in-flow and the out-flow. Be
aware of the support the chair is offering you.
Perhaps let your thoughts drift back to a memory
or a reflection, when you last experienced a sense
of relaxation — however vague the memory — however
vague the reflection. … And, in your own time —
when you're ready to go into hypnosis — let your
eyes open. … *When* you *listen* to these instructions
you will find yourself going quickly and easily
into deep hypnosis and peaceful relaxation. … What
I want you to do is to focus your eyes *here* — on
an imaginary spot in the palm of my hand — as I
move my hand close — *close* your eyes, and as I
move my hand past your nose and chin — take a deep
breath and become beautifully — and deeply
relaxed. Pause for a few moments. I am now going
to lift up your right hand — and *I do not want* you
to help me. What I'm doing is — I'm gently shaking
relaxation into your body — and at the count of
three, I will drop your arm into your lap, and you
will become five times more deeply relaxed. One.
Two. Three."

Next, your left hand will be gently picked up, ensuring the hand
and arm are comfortable. Any reason for not lifting up your
hands will have been discussed with you, say a recent injury, or
religious or personal preferences about being touched.

"That's wonderful!"

Do not be put off by big bunches of praise. Extravagant, voluptuous words are encouraged in hypnosis. These are words of choice encouragement.

> "Now I am going to pick up the other hand — and again — I do not want you to help me. What I'm doing is — I'm shaking even more relaxation into your body. In a moment I will count from one to three, and at the count of three I will drop your hand into your lap and you will become five times more deeply relaxed. One. Two. Three. Doubly *more* relaxed. … That's wonderful! I am now going to place my thumb on your forehead. What I am doing is — I am locking your eyes from the outside, and what I want you to do, is to lock your eyes from the inside. You can do this quickly and easily all by relaxing the tiny muscles around your eyelids. Relax them so much so — that your eyes cannot be bothered to open. In fact, the more you try to open them, the more tightly shut they become. Now — when you are *absolutely sure* that your eyes are so tightly shut, that you simply cannot be bothered to open them. Try them."

The Elman induction is called 'a closed-eye process'. You will attempt to open your eyes and they will not open. Alternatively, you will not even try. Both behaviours are correct.

> "That's fine, you can stop trying now."

Yes, you can open your eyes. It is true you may feel *as if* you cannot. Such is the deliciousness of the state that you have a disinclination to open them, and will preferably keep them shut. Many people have never experienced such a level of relaxation before. To check you really are in control, a very small number of you do 'prise' your eyes open — and that's absolutely fine. You can open your eyes at any time. You are in control. The words of the induction can be repeated. And over the years I have realised some clients are in hypnosis and still open their eyes. This response is simply your way. And there is no wrong way. I have come to this realisation through observation of clients' facial features: relaxed cheeks, lips and jaw, for example. Your breathing changes and slows down. That your fingers and thumbs may involuntarily flick is also evidence of a relaxed state. Experience helps your therapist read the signs. The induction continues as follows:

> "In a moment I will ask you to open your eyes. I
> will count from one to three and click my fingers
> and your eyes will snap shut and become doubly
> more relaxed. Open your eyes. One. Two. Three."

Click of fingers. The eyes will usually open with few exceptions. However, some of you may attempt to open your eyes without success — and when they do not open it is because you do not want to open them or have a disinclination to do so. Remember — you *can* open them.

> "Wonderful! Enjoy that deep, deep sense of
> relaxation. Nothing bothers you. Nothing
> disturbs you. All outside sounds aid and guide

```
you deeper — even deeper — into peaceful
relaxation."
```

So there you have it.   In a safe, relaxing respectful environment you can be helped to enter the hypnotic state easily and effortlessly. There are many, many different inductions and it is likely your hypnotherapist will use an induction other than the one included here.   All are supportive in helping clients into hypnosis, and some will be preferred more than others — by you, and by your hypnotherapist.   Inductions vary in length — the lengthier ones are called progressive inductions.   Essentially the words —   using repetition and monotony seek to encourage relaxation from the top of your head to the tips of your toes, or vice versa. Most relaxation tapes, and in-flight airline recordings employ a form of words that suggest you progressively relax in this way. Additionally they include words and phrases to suggest and encourage well-being, health, and relaxation for the duration of the flight. Progressive inductions are re-assuring, and gentle. And they do induce hypnosis. For those of you who have listened to any relaxation tape — you will discover that you already do have some sense of how you are going to feel.

After the induction comes the deepener.   Whereas the induction places you into a trance state, the deepener takes you to a deeper trance, where useful work can be done. Again, there are many different deepener scripts in use, and this is just one of the three that I regularly use.   There may well be changes to the wording of the script, such as substituting "couch" for "chair", but the key features of the script will remain the same, simply because this script happens to work well. I am including the full text here primarily as illustration, to show you that there is nothing secret or mysterious involved in going into a deeper trance.

The active ingredient of the deepener is your imagining yourself going downwards, which is symbolically linked with the deeper trance state. Some alternative scripts, which I also use, employ an elevator instead of a staircase, or the idea of shells drifting downwards in water. One reason for varying the script is that a client may feel uncomfortable with being inside the enclosed space of an elevator, or may have issues around water.

The script avoids being tied to any particular sense, such as sight. Some people have a vivid visual imagination, others find it easier to sense the presence of things without conjuring up mental pictures. What strengths your own personal imagination has, the deepener script will work with your own individual imagination to lead you into a comfortable depth of trance.

THE STAIRCASE DEEPENER SCRIPT

```
"Imagine yourself standing at the top of a
beautiful staircase  — a staircase, with
ornamental embellishments and decoration.  (Hold
onto a handrail if you wish.)  You're standing on
the top stair — the tenth stair — standing calm —
standing brave — standing confident.  Exactly as
you now choose to be.  As I count down from nine
to one — sense yourself stepping down — safely
down — deeper and deeper down — to the very
basement of relaxation.  Stepping down now.  Nine.
...  Eight.  Deeper and deeper relaxed. …  Seven.
```

```
Six.  Deep and deeper into relaxation.  Five.
Four.  Doubling the relaxation.  Three.  So calm,
so relaxed.  Two.  One.  Now at the very basement
of relaxation.  So calm — so relaxed — so free.
Nothing bothers you — nothing disturbs you.  All
outside sounds aid and guide you.  Deeper — even
deeper — into peaceful relaxation.  And notice, a
little way ahead of you, is a favourite chair.
Sense yourself walking towards that chair — and
relaxing down.  And, the more you relax down — the
better you feel.  And the better you feel — the
more you relax down.  And as you breathe in — you
breathe in positive thoughts.  And as you breathe
out — you breathe out negative thoughts — leaving
more room for more positive, more empowering
thoughts.  So calm.  So relaxed.  So free."
```

Allowing the therapy to be guided by your vocabulary is crucial to the process of interactive hypnotherapy. The deepener respects this, and incorporates the key verbal ingredients you have given to the therapist — perhaps with respect to progress in an earlier session, or words and phrases that you used in declaring your desired outcome, or most likely phrases you employed at the initial session. You may report that you have been "calmer", "much braver" and "more confident" at work since the preceding session. These are 'labels' to be acknowledged, celebrated and declared — further strengthening your renewed and restoring sense of self. These are often new labels to be worn regularly today and in the future — designer labels for your mind, of your own design.

We may sum up this chapter by recalling that the trance state itself is a perfectly natural, everyday condition that your mind goes in and out of easily without ado. Deeper trances require a deliberate process of focused relaxation, usually assisted by an imagined sequence of descent. The hypnotic state is thus the same kind of thing as everyday trance, but more deeply relaxed.

I'm afraid of **hypnosis** but I don't **know why**

98

5
◎

UNDER THE INFLUENCE
Hypnosis in society and culture

◎ "I hope you booked me in for the brainwashing package!" — a client's quip, from one who wanted to get in control of her eating habits.

So you think hypnosis is dangerous? So you think that you will open yourself to the subtle suggestions of your hypnotherapist? And that hypnosis will mess with your mind? If so, then it is time to wake up to the many clandestine influences in our modern-day society, a barrage of subtle suggestions that really do mess with the mind day after day. Suggestions abound!

Richard Mowbray, when discussing the authoritarian nature of cults and cultish developments in society wrote in his book, *The Case Against Psychotherapy Registration* (1995)

"... so with hypnosis, suggestion, and subliminal influence. These are not techniques confined to the 'therapy' room. Our culture is awash with appeals deliberately aimed to bypass conscious awareness. Our media are full of subliminal cues and emotive inducements and our politics full of 'feel-good factors'."

It can be difficult to have a mind of one's own, when one is surrounded and bombarded with many outside influences that suggest what we should say, think, do, eat, wear, and how we smell, and even how we might feel about our smells.

We sometimes describe ourselves as 'open to suggestion' — with respect to what kind of food to eat, which restaurant to go to, which film to see. And we think that our being open to suggestion stops there — within the bounds of our control.

The power of suggestion presses in upon us in every corner of our social life. Suggestion, without any preliminary hypnotising, is carried out on each and every one of us every day in differing ways, and to differing degrees of depth. Suggestion is packaged into the polemic of parents, teachers, politicians, spin doctors, advertisers and marketers, singers, rap artists, preachers, the medical profession and the legal profession, and reporters and news readers in sometimes similar and sometimes differing ways. Our consciousness is sucked into other peoples' creations, which condition and influence our thoughts and our ideas.

People who are good at selling are sometimes described as having 'the gift of the gab' — the gift of words to sell. Product demonstrators so skilled and effective at their craft, and their spiel, can quite dazzle the gathered audience into buying something that, on arriving home, they know they'll never use, or could well have done without.

People who take to the floor to speak to groups often adopt certain tones and modulations of the voice that appeal irresistibly to our hearing. This is the art of rhetoric, an art that has been taught to orators from Socrates' time onwards. And, as Socrates protested — the skill of leading people to believe this or that was often at variance with revealing the truth. So we may fear that the current day rhetorician holds a comparable enthusiasm for persuading their audiences by any means possible. Lawyers and barristers, summing up in court adopt an elegant eloquence, and a distinct way with words — sometimes seeming to argue rationally for the most irrational judgement on a case. Successful street-wise politicians adroitly mould and manipulate the beliefs and opinions of their crowd. And, most pervasive of all, the faceless masters of televisual advertising subtly shepherd consumers towards the checkout till.

In this chapter, we will touch on some ways in which we are collectively subjected to streams of systematic suggestions from various sources. This is a broad subject in its own right. Nevertheless, this quick tour helps to place interactive hypnotherapy in perspective, for the analytical and therapeutic use of hypnosis can help us to roll back the web of subtle suggestions that surrounds us on all sides. It can do so in two ways. First, by enabling us to be aware of what external suggestions we have already adopted, albeit unconsciously, as 'life sentences'. Second, by empowering us to set up internal suggestions of our own making to combat and transcend the ones that have come from sources outside ourselves.

We rely on reporters to tell us what is going on in the world. We trust them to report factually and without distortion. But news readers, particularly on cable networks, but even on national broadcasts, adopt a light-hearted tone in their manner of imparting and of telling the news of the day. Undue emphasis is habitually placed on the filler words linking the serious matter. An upbeat lilt pervades the whole news show — so that a war, an earthquake, or a football match, are all reported with the same uniform mock-gravitas. What we hear in the telling of news stories today is an insidious spin — a form of locution that diverts the average listener's attention away from what is really being said. The news show is often more like a piece of stylised theatre than a delivery of information. Neutral and factual language is replaced by formal codes: for example, the killing of a human being becomes either 'collateral damage' or a ' terrorist outrage'. The meaning of the message assumes a wholly different character. We have listened. We have wondered what we have heard. The words and the way they were delivered have dissolved the emotional impact, and the serious nature of the content. The story is often so superficial and the banter so obvious, that there is a seeming absence of engagement with reality. The sense of the newsreader's disengagement with the matter in hand is reinforced by the use of auto-cues, so that the reader cannot read and digest that material before speaking it to the unseen audience. With eyes fixed upon the camera, words are spoken in a way that is somehow out of tune with the news story. Away from the news desk, the irregular delivery is accompanied to the drumming movement of staccato-like hand gestures that jut out unnaturally as the delivery unfolds. News reporters can appear to deliver scripted bulletins, devoid of any outward signs of emotional cognizance.

There is rather more to this issue than the widely acknowledged observation that we are collectively becoming ever more immune to the remote suffering that we see on our screens. For, in fact, what is present in *The News* is massively sanitised. This issue is about what we hear, and what the media authorities do not want us really to hear, and how the listening public is subtly steered from the one to the other.

Suggestions that are made by television personalities, particularly in coverage that is repeated throughout the day, will lodge as subtle suggestions of opinion. They are planted as ready-made substitutes for personal opinions that might otherwise have to be arrived at by the normal process of assessing evidence and generally thinking about things. So frequently repeated are these verbal slogans that they fly in the face of independent thought. Like a labour-saving device, they obviate the viewer having to expend the time, effort, and uncertainty of exercising the memory and bringing accumulated past experience and wisdom to bear on the present circumstances. The medium is conveying a persistent message that it is not the viewer's business to deliberate about what is really going on behind the sound bite and the spin of the day. The 'Yellow peril' and the 'war against global communism' spun from the past — have now been ousted by 'Islamic fundamentalism' and ' the war against terrorism' in a lexicon devoid of nuance. You need not trouble yourself with the perspectives of foreigners if you adopt the current demonising of 'the enemy'. Instead of trying to articulate complicated human conflicts, the infotainment industry feeds us stylised expressions such as 'peace process', 'surgical strike', 'under siege', and 'shuttle diplomacy'. Just make sure you are up to date with the latest pigeonholing, for today's ally may be tomorrow's evil axis.

Could it be that news events have taken on the mantle of commodities, alongside tangible consumer goods? Could it be that world events are branded and marketed? Just as a beverage marketeer reflects thus on his company's products, "How can I arrange all our communications so that our brand is seen as a 'party spirit' by young consumers, so that they order it in pubs and bars on a Friday and Saturday night?" so also opinion shapers reflect thus, "How can I arrange all our communications on this channel so that this world event is promoted, and perceived in the way that best meets our political alignment?"

As the political spin-doctors learn ever more tricks from their brothers in the advertising industry, we can expect world events to be 'sold' to us in ever more sophisticated ways. The naïve notion that democracy is about politicians serving the people's will is twisted into the cynical notion that the electorate is a market to be sold political events.

A new method of marketing analysis is offered by Media-DNA, a consortium of large corporations in the British marketing and advertising arena[2]. Essentially it involves interviewing a large number of people (5000 in the first wave) and asking them to rank each of the popular advertising vehicles (newspapers, magazines, and television and radio programmes) in respect of each of fifty-one qualities about personality (kind, clever, sentimental), image (British, glamorous, sexy), and positioning (lifts my mood, influences my opinions). The resulting profile is supposed to characterise each medium as a vehicle for advertising, in something like the way that a people's DNA, or genetic make-up, characterises their appearance. Advertisers will then buy advertising space in the media that supposedly match their product. We are 'targeted' (in the advertising industry's curiously revealing word) with advertising that is increasingly precisely honed in to our personal preferences.

A similar process is already underway in Hollywood. For example, directors of war films who are considered to be 'on-message' are given privileged access to military advice and kit. Scott Ridley, in his film *Black Hawk Down* sold the American military intervention in Somalia in just the way the Pentagon wanted, nicely branded as 'humanitarian', and was rewarded with unfettered access to US Army helicopters, bases, and advisers that gave the film its terrific buzz of realism.

How long before news programmes cease to have a primary job of objectively reporting events, and become media

---

[2] BskyB, News International, Capital Radio, Zenith Media, and soon Yahoo.

vehicles in which events are sold by political spin doctors who match the 'media DNA' of the news channel to the political event? This already happens when 'news events' are literally sold to newspapers.

How is it that the cable news networks have anchor people who all appear to talk with a similar voice – energised and optimistic – a similar tone and a similar upbeat tempo? Listen to the beat, and you will not consciously hear the words. Another leaf from a marketing bible perhaps? So-called 'voice-fit' research has shown that a fitting voice is most important in communicating specific claims for products and brands. Perhaps the modern purveyors of political products and brands spread the word with a tone and a tempo so as to deliberately by-pass conscious awareness. Do they want us to wake up from the collective trance and smell the coffee? Of course not.

The recurring motif in all these examples is that there is an industry of skilled practitioners busily exposing you and everybody else to carefully crafted subtle suggestions. A fear of hypnotherapy begins to look a little ridiculous when you see that you are already immersed in a sea of suggestions.

Over here in England, too, the often-repeated headlines and opinions that are generated by spin-doctors seem to be so readily adopted as our very own. There was a small but perfectly formed example of this in Britain during the years 1999 and 2000. Lest we forget the debacle of the Dome, let us now praise famous construction projects. Oft-repeated opinions of the British media persuaded the masses that the Dome was a total disaster zone. In the year of the Dome, you could hear almost every member of the chattering classes — the most sophisticated and intelligently critical of people — state vehemently with spleen and derision that the Dome was a disaster. When prompted, they would admit defensively that, of course, they had never been to the Dome and had no idea what was inside it, and had no desire to know what was inside it. For, since everybody already *knew* that the Dome was a disaster, what was the point of finding out anything about this white elephant? Every newspaper you picked up ridiculed the Dome. Every friend and colleague you spoke to bemoaned the waste of money. Why trouble yourself with facts when you have the same opinion as everyone else? During the last months of the Dome's millennial year, the public relations specialists ironically acknowledged that the editorial copy and features of their journalistic colleagues had programmed the majority of the masses towards a mindset that hated the mere mention of 'the Dome'. The very people whom the PR creatives relied upon to spin positive copy had hosed down the Dome with negativity. The creatives latterly declared "If you have a mind of your own, take it to the Dome". That copy-line played wonderfully to the audience of disgruntled people saying, "I *knew* they shouldn't have spent all that money..." The copy heralded a wake-up call, the hoped-for response being "How dare they imply I do not have a mind of my own!"

The barrage of suggestions starts to get personal if you are yourself a member of one of the groups that the authority figures are demonising. If you are bombarded by confidently expounded suggestions that you are a second-class citizen then it is an uphill struggle to avoid adopting that belief. Until the explosion of consciousness-raising in the 1970s, individuals in Britain or America who wanted to progress with a career had to carry with them an internalised baggage of self-critical suggestions if they were women or members of ethnic minorities. In a myriad ways, women were given subtle hints and suggestions, and often quite explicit declarations, that conveyed a message of 'less than' and 'lack', and tacit disapproval of women who stepped over the domestic line, compounded by the legal position of the time, laws that further kept women in their place.

Hell hath no ingenuity like a man threatened with losing his pay differential. As fast as British equal-rights legislation could demand the same pay for the same job, whether it be done by man or woman, the menfolk would create split job titles sooner than split hairs. Of course, men and women computer programmers should be paid at the same rate as each other, but senior programmers (a more manly role, which would not suit the fair sex) were paid more than junior programmers.

The natural tendency of the human mind is to absorb and internalise suggestions that are made uniformly, emphatically, and with complete confidence by respected persons and organisations. Until the 1970s in Britain, you would find that in almost every job you had, your boss would be a white male; your MP would be a white male; your GP would be a white male; your solicitor was a white male. On mid-afternoon radio, you would be listening to the repeated refrain: "Keep young and beautiful, if you want to be loved." In the toyshops you could choose between Action Man's Jeep and Cindy's dressing table. In school, the boys were acquainted with the engines of industry while the girls were taught how to serve up good food for their future husbands. Confronted by all this and more, the natural response of the subconscious is to take the hint and really believe in one's own inferiority.

In the 1970s, a popular political movement grew up that led people to shift their focus inwards and discover that they had internally absorbed the suggestions of a comprehensively oppressive societal organisation. The result of this, combined with more conventional political activism, was a sea-change in the relative status of the social groups inside and outside the charmed circle of the white males.

Not all groups became politicised, and benefited from consciousness-changing campaigns. My client Joan grew up believing she was a bad person because she had internalised adverse suggestions about being left-handed.

Most often, people are subjected to quite arbitrary patterns of suggestion, which arise out of the personal history of the individuals who are doing the suggesting. Sometimes the patterns are purely verbal, sometimes they are backed up with coercion. My client Trevor grew up believing himself to be 'crap' because of a father whose temper was on a hair-trigger, and who beat him up for the least infringement of his father's rules.   An NSPCC television advertisement campaign in 2001 fused cartoon imagery with real life action to drive home the reality of physical and verbal abuse.   A cartoon boy was seen 'bouncing back' from relentless physical and verbal attacks by his father, but after the final blow he transformed into a real child lying motionless on the floor.   The message reads *Real Children Don't Bounce Back. If you think a child is being abused — do something.*

Interactive hypnotherapy is a way forward for *you* to begin to bounce back, albeit later in your adult life. It encourages you to acknowledge how well you have come through — all things considered. It offers a process through which you may be guided and gently coached to come up with some bright ideas. It leads you to conceive tailor-made suggestions that honour the best and the brightest in you. It helps you to create your own words, your own labels, and your own opinions of yourself — and to let go of those words, labels, and opinions that do not serve you. This kind of hypnotherapy contrasts with the dominant cultural programming that suggests that you should simply wear those designs that are 'spun' and ' doctored' for you.   It bolsters you against the battery of suggestions targeted directly at you through the sophisticated advertising and marketing media. You are guided to source your own suggestions for change.

The source of suggestibility lies in giving exclusive attention to the ostensible message of one medium, be it television, a mobile phone or a computer game. External suggestions are able to take root only when they are not being watched. How often have you seen advertisements on television and thought, "How could anyone be so suggestible as to be persuaded by that"? Those advertisements, however, were not aimed at you. It's the advertisement that's aimed specifically at you that you need to guard against, because that's the one whose suggestions are designed to slip unnoticed into your mind. If you never cook, then an advertisement for a super-duper kitchen gadget will not leave you itching for your credit card; if you never switch on a computer, an advertisement for a super-duper teradrive will pass you by as technojunk. If, however, your own personal interest is triggered, then your attention is switched on and focused on what the advertiser is putting in the foreground. That is when the subtle suggestion in the background slips surreptitiously into your subconscious. The next thing you know is that you have a seemingly genuine desire to buy the advertised product. Of course, it is just coincidence that this desire was kindled after the advertisement. For, you *know* that you are impervious to the suggestiveness of advertisements — after all, you saw right through all those other advertisements for gadgets that are not relevant to you. Phoebe *knows* that she is unaffected by advertising because she has repeatedly passed over advertisements for laptops and desktops and has never had a twinge of desire to buy one; so she knows that the sudden longing to buy the latest 'must-have', ' be-seen-in', ' look-a-like' skin cream, as seen in a current monthly magazine is entirely at her own genuine behest, and is not driven by suggestions planted in her mind by the fashion and cosmetic advertisers.

Suggestions from outside, from society at large, are enabled to influence you without you being able to control them because you did not notice them. Unless you guard your senses and open yourself to the world selectively and maintain a broader attention to what is coming in, you cannot switch the suggestions off.

Like cockroaches scurrying across your floor in the dark of night, the insidious suggestions of the advertising industry rely on their cloak of invisibility. They rely on the oldest trick known to confidence tricksters the world over: the distracted punter is a walkover.

In the past our concentration on these things was limited to the radio and the silent movies. Then followed black and white television, the transistor radio, the gramophone player, the record player, the colour television, the Walkman with tape, compact disc, and mini-disc, the computer, and computer games, the mobile phone, the internet, and e-mail.

All of these media concentrate the attention on one thing. Protracted watching and listening can induce a mild trance-like state of mind.

Television is masterful at maintaining a stranglehold on the mind's attention, and over-stimulating the senses. You may have heard of 'zombie TV'. You may be a regular subscriber and imbiber of zombie TV, or know someone who is. For when you position yourself on the sofa with a free flow of programmes or surf from channel to channel you effectively tune-in to a trance state. In this heightened state of awareness the subconscious records and absorbs messages and communications across the board. It does not discern particularly what goes in. Television coaxes the conscious mind to give all its attention to one single thing, so no attentiveness is available to scan what else is coming in. Consequently, the subconscious mind is exposed and comes forward. This more open part of the mind is generously receptive to the suggestions and product news that bombard the senses during the commercial breaks. These are messages that, depending on your state of viewing, you do not necessarily filter.

Televisual persuaders also rely on the mind's inclination to stay in a blissed-out state. One of the characteristic features of the trance-like state is that it has its own momentum. You do not need to exert any effort to remain in a trance. Once you are entranced, you will stay entranced until you make the effort to get out of it. This fact is a blessing for you if you induced your own trance with prayer, meditation or yoga, but it is a blessing for the advertisers if the television induced the trance. The most common reason for viewers to watch any given television show or commercial is that they were watching whatever was on previously. The television advertising industry is sustained by the massive inertia of a nation glued to its television screens for hours on end, disinclined to hit the off-button on the remote control simply because it is in a blissed-out trance-like state.

Access through the half-seeing eye of the consumer is also a route taken by traumatic scenes in television and film. Scenes and images go directly to your subconscious. There they are lodged, and not necessarily for your advantageous benefit. This diet for the mind can be thought of as being 'toxic', and can ultimately be more devastating than bad food. The latter can be rejected by the body, but television's diet for the mind can lay in the pit of the mind, waiting to emerge in an inappropriate emotional or physical way. Children especially are sensitive in this way, absorbing everything.

Advertisers are aware of how 'open' you are to their suggestions when you watch television or sit down in front of a cinema screen. For this reason, the marketers encourage these states to embed purchase suggestions.

Trance states induced whilst the consumer is driving — more familiarly called autopilot — allow hoardings to embed their suggestions within our subconscious minds. You are driving. Slowly. In a traffic jam. Your attention is caught. You gaze upon a louvre-style advertising hoarding as it flutters across your field of vision — an image and a message — one that perhaps exactly matches your field of dreams? This image is embedded in the blink of an eye.

Now companies are set to download advertisements and purchasing 'suggestions' down the phone line (the WAP technology). They are 'blissfully' aware of how open our minds are to suggestions when entering into communication with these tools. Our consumerist society is driven by hypnotic-like suggestions induced via eye-candy media. The suggestions are not of our design or our own making. Under the bombardment of so much 'cultural hypnosis', is it any wonder some would say it is difficult to think their own thoughts?

When we relinquish control of our own thoughts we become subservient. We open our minds to whatever product seeds the advertiser or persuader wishes to plant. Meditation and hypnotherapy can help you to regain control of your thoughts. You can then let in thoughts of the kind that you would wish to have — enabling you to be able to make the right choices intuitively, and to think more and more the thoughts that will help to create balance and strength in your mind. In meditation, as well as in interactive hypnotherapy, your thoughts are home-grown. What kind of mind-garden do you wish to grow? The choice is always with you. The choice is yours — to seed and nurture a healthy root system, or to turn a blind eye to weeds settling in and strangulating the flowers that you would prefer to see blossom and bloom. In a session of interactive hypnotherapy, you get to design the suggestions that are to be installed within your subconscious mind. You get to choose and to suggest, and to embed, the words and the phrases that best reflect the feelings and the values that you, as an individual, wish to govern your personality.

So often, people come to hypnotherapy with an already in-depth knowledge of their problem, and sometimes they come with an insight into how their own thinking — their own habits of thought — may be contributing to the problem, and how they could be making it worse. "I'm my own worst enemy!" "I know I get myself wound up!" Talking about blushing, one client report-ed, "It can happen at the drop of a hat. If a question is directed towards me, I feel embarrassed. I think, 'Oh no! I'm going to go red.' It happens because I've told myself it is going to happen!"

This is so true. As we think, so often we are. If we think we can, then we can. Moment by moment, our inner thoughts create suggestions. The more negative a thought, the faster it is. These uncontrolled suggestions can work as a power for positive good, and most definitely they can also work to disempower and wreak harm. Our thoughts are a diet for the mind. We 'are' the thoughts that we digest. More positive thoughts flow through a quieter mind.

Erich Fromm in his book *Having and Being* promulgated the message in the 1970s that 'being' is more important than 'having'. In 2001, car drivers in England were presented with the contrary message, in a hoarding that proclaimed that having one particular model of car was more important than being. Perhaps invoking the legal precedent that possession is nine-tenths of law, its copy-line under a sexy pose of the car was, "Possession is everything".

In interactive hypnotherapy, the client is king. The client chooses what to discard from the mind; what to keep; and what is to be created anew, remembered and reaffirmed.

Another wonderful thing about hypnotherapy is that whatever specific area of life, or challenge, that you come to work on, you will very likely find that your sense of self-confidence and self-esteem tend to soar. Positive outcomes create a ripple effect into other areas of your life. You may have come to the hypnotherapy session with a wish-list, and discover that some of those wishes are granted with barely a mention, because they were tied up with other things. You may find that some outcomes are an unexpected but delightful surprise.

6

◎

PROFESSIONALISM IN PRACTICE
Excluding hypnotherapy from the medical canon

More and more people are becoming aware of the benefits of hypnotherapy, and current thinking is evolving towards a more positive and true appreciation of its usefulness. Nevertheless, many clients are a little nervous when they arrive at the hypnotherapy practice for the first time. They are very glad and excited to come, and have often been considering the prospect of hypnotherapy for some time. But they are human, and humans can get nervous at first-time events, especially with the crosscurrents of uninformed aspersions that are cast on hypnotherapy.

People associate hypnotherapy with what they have seen on television and on the stage, or what they have heard at second hand about stage hypnosis. They believe they may lose control; may be humiliated; embarrassed; or reveal a secret. They fear that they will not remember what happened to them and they sometimes fear their vulnerability. Many clients have remarked, "With something like hypnosis, you have to go to someone you can trust."

Understandably, vulnerability is an issue for all clients. Why? Clients say, "Because my eyes are closed". "I am scared that something could happen whilst I am 'sleeping'." "You have to be one hundred percent comfortable with the person". Comments like these are especially common with female clients. The press and other media have, from time to time run stories of rogue hypnotherapists in the field, and sadly some of these reports have been true.

These events cast doubt on the professional status of hypnotherapists, and cast a shadow in the minds of those who might otherwise have benefited from the extraordinary and positive transformations that can be achieved.

I believe that these occurrences are rare. Of course, the newspapers will pack more critical language into reports of rogue hypnotherapists than into reports of deviant consultants or GPs. If a GP abuses the trust placed in him, then the implied view is not that general medical practice is a dubious thing, but that some individuals fail to maintain the required standards. If a hypnotherapist similarly abuses her client's trust, the media tend to tar the whole profession with the same brush. Needless to say, this does not serve the consumers of the news with a balanced and objective perspective.

Rogue hypnotherapists will increasingly become rarer in the future. Professional hypnotherapy bodies are becoming ever more rigorous in their criteria for admitting practitioners, and more rigorous in their demands on professional practice. I recently had reason to contact a professional body, one to which a hypnotherapist belonged. The hypnotherapist had attempted to take advantage of a male client in a highly vulnerable state. The client was experiencing a debilitating level of anxiety, and had been asked to pay for a minimum of ten sessions up front. Furthermore he was told that the therapy would not work until the tenth session, after which the therapist would not see him again. I was appalled and disappointed by his experience. Appalled because clients can experience relief in remarkably fewer sessions, and sometimes even one session. (Miracles do happen!) Particularly, though, I was disappointed for the profession, whose image is being sullied by a few irresponsible individuals.

As the therapist involved in this case was advertising as part of a group in a national directory, I contacted the professional body concerned. They unreservedly commended my call, and even went so far as to say that had I not reported the incident for investigation, I would have been flouting my professional obligations as a hypnotherapist.

Your comments and experiences do indeed matter to professional organisations, and any complaint is logged against the therapist. When there are problems with a practitioner in the field, you would not necessarily be the only client to have experienced conduct unbecoming the profession. Because of strict standards of confidentiality, you cannot be informed of any previous reports. (While primarily seeking to protect the client from the rogue hypnotherapist, the professional body has a commensurate duty not to publicise potentially false accusations from disgruntled clients.) Nevertheless, be assured that your comments do have an effect and do help to keep professional standards high.

Some potential clients are put off by such experiences, or what they hear of them at third hand, and steer clear of hypnotherapy altogether. When the aforementioned client eventually found me, he telephoned to ask whether what he had experienced was normal practice, and to seek some confirmation and reassurance. Of course I was in a position to do that and I was glad that he had continued to keep hold of the thought that hypnotherapy could help stabilise his emotional state.

Keep in mind there are practitioners of varying levels of expertise in all professions. Professional hypnotherapy does not come as 'a business in a box' together with a '30-day action plan', and a correspondence course. Professional electricians are not born electricians, they are trained electricians, although some have more of a talent than others. Likewise hypnotherapists, but even with training, hypnotherapists do vary in their abilities. Some simply have more aptitude for the job than others, or they may be better suited to working with some kinds of people and with some kinds of problems than others. Just as you may seek a second opinion from a doctor or a consultant, or get a recommendation for a builder, a plumber, or an accountant, before contracting them to commence work on your home or your financial affairs, you may seek referrals for a hypnotherapist. Discuss the nature of your interest in hypnotherapy with each of them, and get a sense of how you feel they respond to you. It is quite acceptable to ask questions — to ask about training, to ask how long the therapist has been practising and to which professional body she belongs. You can then request a telephone number to make further enquiries if you wish. Every professional body has a code of ethics, and this will be supplied to you on request.

General practitioners vary widely as to their understanding of hypnosis and hypnotherapy. Consequently there is much variation in whether they will endorse hypnotherapy sessions for their patients. I gather from young doctors (often, they are trainees who find their way into my practice), that hypnosis receives a cursory mention in medical syllabuses. This position will surely change in the longer-term future.

Social phobia could be described in many different ways. Let us define it in one way — an inability to walk into a room full of people alone. Your diagnosis? Shyness perhaps? And a degree of lack — usually of confidence and self-esteem. Potential cure? Routinely, I find that my clients report that their doctor had suggested some counselling, and a prescription — for Prozac.

"Let's see how you get on with those, and make an appointment in one months time."

Just what the doctor ordered ... For blushing: the antidepressants Seroxat® and Prozac® and the beta-blocker Atenolol. For acute anxiety states: Seroxat® and Prozac®. For feeling unhappy: Seroxat®, Fluoxetine (including the brand Prozac®), and Sertraline (including the brand Lustral®). Clients report doses of

20mg once or twice a day for cases of feeling low, and up to 50mg in serious cases of depression. For insomnia: Diazepam (the generic name for the famous brand Valium®). For fear of flying and public speaking: the beta-blocker Propranolol, and Diazepam. For social phobia: Seroxat®. For blushing: Clonidine (including specifically the brand Dixarit®). For lack of concentration and lack of focus: Ritalin®. For over-eating: Xenical®. For bingeing and over-eating: Reductil®. For smoking: Zyban®. For too much shopping: Cipramil®. (US doctors have decided that 'shopaholism' exists and is an illness, for which Cipramil® pills can be prescribed.) For impotence: Viagra®. Drug prescriptions prevail!

I always ask clients whether they are taking any medical advice or medication. The drugs listed above are typical examples of ones that I have been told were prescribed to clients for the stated reasons, before coming to the session. A typical response is, "I'm taking Seroxat for nervousness and shyness. I have been taking it for two years. I was told it could take a few weeks, but with me it took three months to work. One day, I noticed that I wasn't shy anymore. I used to be afraid all of the time — of being nervous, and of blushing. Now I do not have the physical feelings of nervousness. However, I know I would like to come off the drug, and do it for myself."

We are under the influence of medical priests and their pharmaceutical pushers, always quick to spot a marketing opportunity, and a new formulation. What an influence this combination has! The power of this potent force to invoke a diagnosis, suggest a label — a label spoken by one on high — and the person who has gone to their doctor 'feeling low' with 'shyness', 'anxiety', 'blushing', 'stammering', and an extreme partiality to chocolate is described as 'depressed'. Some protest, "I'm not depressed, I'm not a depressed person".

One client told me: "Since December, I seem to be anxious the whole time. I'm constantly on edge. My doctor put me on a course of anti-depressants. He said that they are beneficial for anxiety. I did actually take one, but the one I took made me spaced out. It numbed me rather than removing the anxiety."

Another: "Apart from the sick feeling in your stomach, your thinking is reduced to a 'zombie-like paralysis' that doesn't allow you to go out and make a living."

More often than not people under the influence of the medical fraternity succumb because the 'suggestion' is made from 'an authority' — one with the designation Doctor, Consultant, Psychiatrist, or Psychologist. We walk away with a written declaration confirming our 'sickness', and further confirming authorisation for us to partake daily of the recognised remedy. Suddenly we are deemed depressed. We walk into the medical arena with blushing and come out depressed! What a difference ten minutes make! How the pharmaceutical shareholders must smile. How easily can some of us accept and act upon suggestion. And you thought hypnosis was dangerous! There are those who hold fast to their power, and do not fall as easy prey. "I said, I'm not depressed. I'm not a depressed person."

These medications cost the National Health Service up to £40 for a 28-day supply (not to mention the administrative overheads). As the pharmaceutical companies' intention is that you continue to take prescribed medications for an extended period of time, and sometimes years, the cost doesn't bear thinking about. Repeat prescriptions can get dished out for years without any apparent monitoring of the individual patient's change in circumstance. One client, looking to reduce her medication, told me that she had been taking Dutonin®, an anti-depressant medication, for five years. She regularly collected a repeat prescription from her doctor's surgery when she went home to Ireland. On no occasion to date, had any enquiry been made, to monitor or re-assess her case notes.

More and more millions thrown down our throats. Not to mention the millions flushed down the loo! Often clients cash in the prescription and then decide, after taking the medication for a couple of days, that they do not like the side effects. "I can't feel doped up for two weeks before the pills start working. I have to go to work and function." More and more millions flushed away!

In the seventies and eighties, one client reported being prescribed a small handful of diazepam tablets a day, to help control his stammering. The relaxing side effects of the medication were intended to slow him down physically and mentally and thus slow down his speech. Indeed the medication worked, but at what a cost! And of course when he eventually weaned himself off them, the stammer was as it always had been. This may be less barbaric than the practice of earlier generations, of physically trimming off part of the stammerer's tongue. But surely we can do better than this!

It must be acknowledged that a prescription may be the most appropriate and the only answer for some serious medical conditions. Nevertheless, one ponders the wisdom of prescribing drugs when a patient seeks help for such 'problems' as blushing, stress, and anxiety. Anti-depressants and beta-blockers are an allopathic answer to what is often caused by an emotional disturbance within.

Increasingly, women and men reach the point where an ever-rising salary and status do not compensate for the lack of time that is left over, after work, to live a life. They realise there is a 'season for all things' and that 'the time of their lives' has been offered up to the corporate altar and devoured by the demands of the corporate gods. They are angry and resentful and are resolved that this pattern will not be continued into their thirties. Prozac is not the answer. Anger generally has a root. Taking Prozac to relieve anger is rather like stepping into your garden and cutting the tops off the dandelions. To all intents and purposes the dandelions are gone. But you have not accessed the emotional root. Interactive hypnotherapy enables people who are experiencing out-of-order emotions and experiences to discover what is the root of the anger — the blushing, the panic, and the shyness. It is not unusual for a client to remark along these lines after hypnotherapy: "I felt like I'd dug up the shyness."

The gifts of hypnotherapy reveal themselves when the hypnotherapist knows intuitively how to choreograph a session to help you feel the way you choose to be — to arrive at a positive result. Healing with hypnotherapy is a practised art, and there are established techniques and procedures that work elegantly, and these too can be learned. Intuition adds another ingredient, one that allows the hypnotherapist to participate fully in your dance, seamlessly and unobtrusively.

What is very important for you to know is that hypnotherapy is generally practised by people who are lay-persons, as opposed to people who are trained psychologists, and psychiatrists — both professions falling into the medical model. Both of the 'psych'-disciplines rely on medication to effect 'cures' and to 'get results', and neither can embrace the wide range of conditions for which hypnotherapy can demonstrably provide cures and result.

Doctors too, do use hypnotherapy. I was excited to discover this early on in my career. I discovered that under the wing of the Royal Society of Medicine is a section of hypnosis and psychosomatic medicine. Although I knew I was not eligible to join, having spoken to the administrator, I did not question that it would be possible to attend the lectures. I was eager to learn more from people who had been practising for years. The talk inspired me and, as I was new to the audience, one of the doctors spotted me. He was a kindly soul, and clearly wished to embrace comers-in. He took me under his wing and invited me to join him as his guest at the dinner to be held before the next evening talk. I was delighted and agreed. He was very pleased I'd chosen to accept, and I was duly seated next to him for dinner. I have no doubt he wished to encourage me, recognising my earnest enthusiasm, respect for, and wonder at the work.

At dinner I sat opposite a female psychiatrist who was an established member of the Society. I asked about her work, she asked about mine. Whereupon she posed the question, "What are you?" I naively replied that I practised interactive, participative hypnotherapy. "No, no", she continued.

"Are you a Psychiatrist?"

"No", I said.

"Well are you a Psychologist?"

"No", I replied. By now, rather nervous and very aware of what was coming and knowing truth was fast losing out, she protested,

"Well what are you then?"

With what must have been a transparently thin veneer of boldness I replied, "I'm a lay hypnotherapist". She could hardly conceal her distaste. Imagine a Jane Austin character blustering about, with buttons about to burst and you will imagine the scene. In the silence I was sentenced.

At the end of the evening, following the talk, the kindly doctor who had invited me, was given the embarrassing task of advising me that it would be appreciated if I did not come again.

Feeling his embarrassment acutely, I graciously acceded to his request.

As I walked back to the London Underground that evening, having followed my heart into hypnotherapy, I felt defeated, and suddenly very aware of the strength needed to endure the journey that lay ahead. In those defining moments the struggle seemed daunting. First the struggle to establish myself within the profession, and second the struggle for the professional lay-hypnotherapists within it, to be recognised as potential allies and friends to the medical and psychiatric profession. Third, to contribute in whatever way I could to encourage and promote the respectable face of hypnosis and hypnotherapy.

When your professional competence is called into question in this way, you inevitably stop for a moment and reflect on how you know that you are competent. Now, a moment is all it takes to flick through several years of case notes and encounter the reassuring objective fact that hundreds of people have benefited substantially and quickly from what is dismissively labelled 'lay hypnotherapy'. For the medical profession to dismiss an entire discipline that is daily striving for the positive benefit of clients indicates a highly subjective bias on their part. At the time of this particular meeting, however, I had only recently embarked on my career in hypnotherapy. Lacking, then, the backing of a track record of satisfied clients, I had only my intuition to rely on. And my intuition was that a loving and caring approach to clients was more likely to get results than an uncritical adherence to the formalities of the establishment. This is not a peculiarity of hypnotherapy. Even within the establishment, evidence-based medicine is fighting increasingly successful battles against entrenched preconception in many areas.

The British Society of Medical and Dental Hypnosis continues to hold much the same view, which was summarised in a telephone call I made to them, in the course of my research: "You are not a clinical psychologist, a medical practitioner or a dental practitioner. It is a medical and dental society. The rules are very strict. Only medically trained practitioners can attend our meetings. You are not one of the medical or the dental fraternity. Within the realms of our society we couldn't possibly train lay-hypnotherapists. You have to have standards. We have to be so careful. We have to work within our own jurisdiction. You know stage hypnotists are constantly being sued, and we cannot take those risks. We train only our own people."

I completely and absolutely agree that standards of care are paramount. Such standards are fundamental to the ethics of the leading professional bodies for lay hypnotherapists. Indeed, the Hypnotherapy Society has participated in the process that led to the development of National Occupational Standards for Hypnotherapy. There are ongoing moves towards voluntary self-regulation. Professional bodies are modernising, are increasingly open and honest in dealing with complaints, setting standards, and registering therapists." The desire is "to see hypnotherapy as a trustworthy and mature profession, and organisations such as

The Hypnotherapy Society (HS), registering therapists and accrediting training in a reliable way." Neither the Hypnotherapy Society nor any other present hypnotherapy organisation is endorsed by the government, or any body sponsored by the government. The future endorsement of one or more bodies for the hypnotherapy profession is a long way off, and very much subject to considerable dialogue and negotiation." Further, the Hypnotherapy Society participates — along with other organisations — in the seminars run by the Foundation for Integrated Health, a charity whose mandate is to encourage alternative health organisations to develop responsibility, standards, and models of voluntary self-regulation.

It is of interest to compare the different rates of progress of hypnotherapy and psychoanalysis toward official recognition. In the 1880s, Sigmund Freud (1856-1939) developed an approach involving free association and dream interpretation that became known as psychoanalysis. Whereas modern hypnotherapy can bring about transformation and change in a short period of time, psychoanalysis can often take years.

Elaine Sheehan, in her book *Self Hypnosis*, takes up the story: "In 1891 the British Medical Association appointed a committee to investigate the nature and value of hypnotism. The report that followed declared acceptance of hypnotic phenomena as genuine, and satisfaction that hypnotism could be of use in the therapeutic process. It also advised against its use for the purpose of entertainment." This affirmation was not enough to roll back the tide of fashion, which was emphatically Freudian. Freud had initially tried to use hypnotic suggestion as a symptomatic technique: he tried to implant suggestions to make the patient's symptoms just go away. With this, he had only limited success, and generally only temporary. Freud, and others, realised that the reason that direct suggestion ultimately failed was that it did not locate and remove the root cause of the patient's problem. This is often the case, direct suggestion is a 'blunt' instrument.

Freud's response to this was to develop new, non-hypnotic techniques to locate the underlying cause — namely, free association. At this time, a few other analysts adapted hypnosis into an analytic tool for uncovering the root cause of the patient's problem, but Freud's pre-eminence eclipsed their work.

During the First World War, and again during the Korean War, hypnosis was used to provide a short-term therapy for soldiers suffering from the traumatic effects of the fighting, but hypnotherapy stayed off the mainstream agenda. In so far as hypnosis was studied at all, it was in the field of psychology rather than medicine. Sheehan notes that "the first modern book on the topic was by Clark L Hull (1884-1952) in 1933, and was entitled *Hypnosis and Suggestibility: An Experimental Approach.*

In 1892, and again in 1955, the British Medical Association (BMA) published the reports of committees that were set up to investigate hypnosis. Both committees concluded that hypnosis is an objectively real phenomenon, and that it has therapeutic potential. But it also made a strong pitch for the control of hypnotherapy by the medical establishment. The members of the 1892 committee deemed hypnosis to be a medical procedure, and they recommended that its use be limited to 'medical men'.   In 1955, the new committee members recommended that hypnosis be restricted to "persons subscribing to the recognised ethical code which governs the relation of doctor and patient", adding that this "would not preclude its use by a suitably trained psychologist or medical auxiliary of whose competence the medical practitioner was personally satisfied and who would carry out, under medical direction, the treatment of patients selected by the physician".

Almost fifty years on, and still hypnotherapy continues to be viewed by some as rather curious and rather quack!   From my own experience, it seems rare that doctors who are steeped in the allopathic approach will ever suggest hypnotherapy to their patients. Yet, hypnosis has survived.

Perhaps now it really is making a mark in the minds of the wider public as an alternative, or indeed a complementary way to treat physical and psychological disorders.   Perhaps now it really will be championed by the decision-makers — the movers and shakers in the mainstream modern therapeutic arena — as a way to contribute to the treatment of both physical and psychological disorders. We can do little more than to continue using and developing the technique and to hope that the more empirically minded elements of the establishment will take cognisance of the method's remarkable efficacy as a non-medical mode of therapy.

There is also, however, the political dimension — the question of who should control hypnotherapy. As we saw in the reports of the BMA committees, there is a drive to medicalise hypnosis, that is, to place control of this mode of therapy firmly in the hands of the medical establishment, and where possible to forbid its used by anyone else. It is sometimes proposed that this belies the doctors' desire to maintain a closed shop for the collective benefit of the medical profession. I would attribute that proposition to the over-credulous conspiracy theorists, and I think that the medical people who seek to limit access to hypnotherapy are well-meaning but misguided or misinformed. Take the case of 19th century surgeon, James Esdaile. He practised in India, and as a matter of necessity, performed dozens of operations, including major amputations without anaesthetic and without his patients feeling pain. He claimed a ninety-five per cent success rate, at a time when most surgeons killed some forty per cent of their patients. When he came back to Great Britain and tried to interest his colleagues in hypnosis as an alternative anaesthesia he was laughed out of court by the medical authorities.

Before asking why the medical establishment is so keen to control hypnotherapy, let us first be clear on why hypnotherapy is *not* a medical treatment. Fundamentally, hypnotherapy is a humanistic practice and not a theoretical or knowledge-based practice. The basic skill of leading someone into a state of hypnosis is not rocket science! Truly, it can be learned by almost anyone. The ability to induce hypnosis is not a 'power' that is possessed by some and not by others. Some people will be more effective by virtue of their manner and disposition, and their voice, but the potential is there for most of us. Anyone with the self-confidence and the training could hypnotise another person. Indeed you can learn to help someone into the relaxed state that we call hypnosis in a weekend course. You can buy a book and teach yourself.

What is much more valuable, more difficult to achieve, and where the professional training comes into play, is the bene-ficial and therapeutic use of that hypnotic trance in effecting a change of the mind and behaviour, and in healing. The most essential requirement for doing that is a caring, loving, empathic, and intuitive engagement in dialogue with the client's subcon-scious mind. Interactive hypnotherapy is not driven by a theory of what to say and when to say it. There are guidelines, but there are few diktats.

This is in complete contrast with medicine, which requires the doctor to master a theoretical model of how the physiological and biochemical systems of the body work, how surgical and pharmaceutical interventions have their effects, as well as memorising a phenomenal mass of data about the body and modes of treatment. Medicine is largely a science, hypnotherapy is largely an art. There are two basic reasons for medicine to be kept under the strict control of recognised institutions. First, medical students need to acquire a large body of knowledge and understanding that can be objectively verified. Second, failure to master that knowledge and understanding can be extremely dangerous for the public because the techniques and substances they use are very potent and, if misused, can do great harm. Neither of those two reasons is relevant to hypnotherapy. Successful hypnotherapy relies on humanistic skill that cannot be objectively assessed in an examination hall. And hypnotherapy is very limited in what harm it can do. Interactive hypnotherapy, in particular, is an inherently safe mode of therapy, precisely because it is driven by the client's own suggestions. In so far as hypnotherapy also involves elements that can be objectively assessed and monitored — such as ethically correct relations between therapist and client — it can and should be controlled by a recognised institution on the same lines as medicine is regulated. And in so far as the abuse of hypnosis can be harmful — as in stage hypnosis — it can and should be regulated. But the core activity of hypnotherapy does not lend itself to regulation on the same lines as medical practice. It is a different kind of activity and its standards need to be maintained by different kinds of procedures and institutions. As a humanistic art, hypnotherapy's standards would be better maintained by organisations that model themselves on art establishments such as music schools or art colleges.

An idea that is often put forward by opponents of lay hypnotherapy is that hypnotherapy is dangerous because it may deter someone from seeking medical help for a condition that does need medical treatment. The most common example is that of pain relief. The idea that someone who is suffering from persistent pain from an unknown cause will be content to obtain relief from a lay hypnotherapist rather than seeing a doctor owes more to the imagination than to any real risk. First of all, sheer common sense will inform both client and therapist that physical pain is a message from the body telling the client that something is physically amiss and needs to be addressed. Second, the first part of interactive hypnotherapy seeks to identify the reason for whatever challenge or problem the client is facing. Now, if the client presents with, say, a pain in the lower back, then the most likely explanation is that there is some damage or disorder in the lower back, and that the client should see a doctor. Third, hypnotherapy is not cheap. It is highly unlikely that someone would invest in a series of hypnotherapy sessions when a visit to the general practitioner service that is available free of charge on the NHS is, as we have already noted, the more plausible first port of call for dealing with unexplained pain. Dr Hellmut Karle, formerly a clinical psychologist at Guy's Hospital, London, put some effort into opposing lay hypnotherapy, and wrote in 1991, "a common request to anyone who employs hypnotic techniques in therapy, is for help with chronic pain". Working as a clinical psychologist in a major hospital must surely account for this frequency, for amongst my many hundreds of clients, I have not had any one client who came to me exclusively for help with chronic pain. Hypnosis to help with pain control has always been an adjunct to the primary treatment. In my own practice, surprised clients have often reported that the pain in a specific part of their body had abated or was much reduced. This unexpected outcome then motivated them to explore the use of hypnotherapy for the reduction and alleviation of pain. Some discovered when listening to the audiotape or CD (which I give to clients following the initial session) that the experience of regular relaxation contributed further to easing their discomfort. Improvement in the depth and quality of sleep is a common experience of clients who do find time to do their 'homework'. The depth and quality of sleep is paramount in facilitating healing, allowing the body to restore and regenerate at the deepest possible level. Hypnosis offers a fast-track way to reach this state. This begs comparison with the research of Professor John Gruzelier at Imperial College, London, whom I mentioned earlier.

Another example that is concocted is that of serious mental disorder, such as 'schizophrenia'. The proposition is that an individual who is suffering from psychosis will attend a series of hypnotherapeutic sessions instead of seeking psychiatric help. This scenario is less incredible than the previous one, as serious mental disorder may well distort the client's common sense. Any therapist, however, is pretty quickly going to realise that the client has a major disorder that is beyond the power of hypnotherapy to ameliorate. Carrying out interactive hypnotherapy requires a high degree of motivation and cooperation on the part of the client. A person who is so mentally disturbed as to be unable to attain that degree of motivation and cooperation will simply not be able to engage in hypnotherapy. If, on the other hand, the person has only some comparatively mild disturbance, and is able and willing to engage in hypnotherapy, and if hypnotherapy is successful in helping the client, then we may question the medical establishment's wisdom in seeking to turn the client's problem into something medical, precluding the possibility of an emotional source or root.

As we noted in the previous chapter, creeping medicalisation is deeming ordinary human conditions such as shyness, anxiety, and even fear of public speaking, into medical conditions. They are *not* medical conditions. They are ordinary problems that many healthy human beings face, which hypnotherapy can do a great deal to alleviate and resolve.

These arguments against lay hypnotherapy are all highly contrived, and it would be helpful to bring the discussion back to practical reality. If hypnotherapy were to be handed back to the medical establishment, the result would not be better, or safer, or more efficacious hypnotherapy. The result would almost certainly be very little hypnotherapy at all, as evidenced in some states in America, where managed health care has been detrimental to therapeutic use. Were the same to happen in the U.K. it is likely hypnotherapy would find itself back in a corner gathering dust, as it did for many decades after Freud gave up on it.

Finally, let us ask why doctors are so implacably opposed to lay hypnotherapy. There are, I believe, two general reasons for this. First, there is the medical establishment's general antipathy toward complementary medicine. Second, there are specific features of hypnosis that make it hard for the establishment to embrace.

Much has been written about the medical establishment's hostility toward complementary medicine, and some of it is quite unfair. Conspiracy theorists see it as a deliberate strategy to preserve the establishment's territory. In fact, medical practitioners are incredibly dedicated people who have spent many years in training and work long and hard for the welfare of their patients. They are also, however, the products of a highly conservative educational system. Medical training has to impart a huge amount of knowledge and understanding and has to make sure that medical students get it right. There is no latitude for students to go off and do their own thing. Anything that does not fit into the existing edifice of knowledge is going to be pushed to one side. That, however, is not the end of the story. In order for doctors to maintain their strict adherence to the standard procedures and techniques, in the face of the stress and pressure of daily medical practice, they must internalise a complete conviction in medicine and a corresponding disbelief in any competing approach. This belief system is, if you like, the immune system of the medical profession. In order to maintain the integrity of medical practice, there must be a culture of unquestioning adherence to the established practices. Any deviation is automatically attacked both by the individual doctor's own mind-set and by the expressed opinions of his or her peers. This culture of rigorous standardisation is not, in itself, a bad thing. It is, in fact, necessary for the great edifice of allopathic medicine to flourish. But it does have the side effect of stifling innovation. It is an obstacle for innovation even within conventional medicine, but it places a complete brake on the radical innovation that is proposed in complementary medicine. The one route for innovation is the clinical trial carried out by independent researchers. With a battery of randomised clinical trials supporting a new therapeutic intervention, even the conservative ranks of the medical profession will allow new ideas to come into use. As we shall see in the next chapter, randomised trials of hypnotherapy are few and small, and hypnotherapy is consequently unable to puncture the wall of conservatism that isolates the medical establishment.

There are two further burdens that hypnotherapy in particular has to carry on its long trek toward official recognition.

First, there is the stage hypnotist. Hypnosis is nowadays unique in being the only therapeutic modality that is regularly used for public entertainment. Many years ago, nitrous oxide played a similarly dubious role of being 'laughing gas' for party entertainers, at the same time as being a useful anaesthetic for doctors. In the 1960s, the recreational abuse of psychotropic substances such as lysergic acid diethylamide (LSD) completely destroyed the programme of research into the therapeutic uses of those chemicals. It took thirty-five years for work to restart. As for hypnotherapy, from the first party tricks of F. Anton Mesmer (1734-1815), hypnosis has been tainted by its abuse in public entertainment. Probably the single greatest boost that hypno-therapy could hope for would be the abolition of stage hypnosis!

Second, the speed and efficacy of interactive hypnotherapy is paradoxically a problem, when dealing with conditions that psychiatry also claims for its territory. A psychiatrist who has devoted years to acquiring skills that enable her to tackle a problem slowly if at all, will face a personal challenge when a humanistic method achieves the same or better success quickly. There is a temptation to feel that this devalues the hard-won skill of the psychiatrist, and a natural reaction to that is to be dismissive of hypnotherapy. I think that most psychiatrists will rather see it as revealing a need to redefine the boundaries of psychiatry. Sadly, there are others who go into denial over the power of hypnotherapy and refuse to countenance the possibly that, in some kinds of problem, the pharmacological approach is not the best one for the client.

I'm **afraid** of **hypnosis** but I don't **know why**

7
◎

DOCTOR'S NOTES
Hypnotherapy as last resort

As we have seen, during all those many interim years after the initial interest in hypnotherapy, the pharmaceutical companies got into the race. Drugs won out. Drugs often win out in matters of mental health and well-being. Pharmaceutical products are quick and assumed to be effective. Certainly they have an effect, but what precisely it is remains unclear. Using pills to tackle problems of the mind has been compared to thumping a computer that is malfunctioning. Sometimes it works. Sometimes it nudges something back into place, and the patient can get on with his or her life. But there are no 'silver bullets' in psychiatry.

The compelling story of Dr. John Forbes Nash Jr., the maths genius who battled schizophrenia, portrayed in the film *A Beautiful Mind*, raised awareness and opened a dialogue about one of the least understood, most complex and devastating diseases that exists. The film generated a vigorous debate amongst mental health professionals, dividing them on the truthfulness of the portrayal. Psychologists and psychiatrists took issue with the film, because Nash begins to improve seemingly without medication, relying on the love and support of his wife's dedication as

145

medication, and the power of his own will to control his symptoms. Mental health professionals who applauded this powerful film asserted that, when the disease does strike, compassionate care in a supportive environment, *along with medication and other treatment modalities*, can indeed help pick up the pieces of a broken life.

I have encountered many clients seeking a complementary therapy to overcome depression over the years. Many of these clients had initially approached their GPs, reporting anxiety states to varying degrees, and likewise depression in various states. The majority of these clients were taking medication under the direction of a doctor or a consultant psychiatrist, and one client in particular, with serious depression had been subject to more than a dozen electro-convulsive therapy (ECT) treatments. As a result of them, the depression had not shifted, and his memory in certain areas of his life had been severely affected. Under hypnosis there emerged a theme — one of 'drawing the line' at a certain time of day, before which he was too depressed to function. This was a line that in his presenting condition (before hypnotherapy had started) he had set about drawing each day when he got out of bed. This line was the benchmark for the effective start of his day — a line that he drew around mid-afternoon most days. After three o' clock, he functioned, at least after a fashion. When he came to see me, he had moved back into his parents' house — a home that was supportive, compassionate and caring.

Following the first session of interactive hypnotherapy, he found himself intrigued. He began to draw the line a bit earlier, at around noon — on some days. This aroused curiosity and created for him a body of evidence to support his belief that there had been change in his condition, and that therefore there was a possibility of more change. After the second session he had woken to the realisation of having, figuratively speaking, 'not drawn the line' with a wife who had mentally emasculated him. By the third session of hypnotherapy, the line was drawn at around ten o'clock in the morning — not on every day, but on several days in succession. Now the evidence was mounting. My client warmed to this improvement and his new-found sense of empowerment. So much so, that he telephoned to request that he postpone his next appointment to four weeks hence, as the improvements continued so well. Such is the power of will and of the mind. He began to regain control of himself and his life. He regained access to his power within. He became determined to get better.

For some cases of depression, and even some cases of serious depression, interactive hypnotherapy is a valid treatment modality, alongside medication for an appropriate time — that can help to pick up the pieces of a temporarily fractured life. The depression can begin to lift and to transform as the client gets back into the driving seat, and assumes a more participative role in the treatment for his case. He takes back a feeling of control by shifting gear — in the engine in his mind.

The leading UK-based mental health charity, Mind, has championed this view with respect to its own campaign. In 2002, Mind launched *My Choice*, a campaign aimed at improving the level of choice of treatments available to people with mental health problems from their GP and health services. In Mind's view, individuals with mental health problems respond best where there is a whole range of treatments available, including counselling, exercise and complementary therapies, alongside medication.

The human mind is an enormous hubbub of different players, each one a complicated thing in its own right. A drug is a blunt instrument that promotes or demotes whole teams of mental players, pushing them around, without attempting to engage in dialogue with them. This may be the only way to handle an emergency, or if the players mutiny so badly that they become ungovernable. But, for people with chronic and less severe problems, drugs are not the only approach, and may not be the best.

The big institutions of psychiatry favour drugs for several reasons. They are convenient to use, but also lend themselves to clinical trials. The randomised, placebo-controlled, double-blind clinical trial is the gold standard for assessing the worth of any medical intervention. In these trials, a large group of patients are randomly allocated to take either the real pill or a dummy pill (the 'placebo'), and neither the patient nor the doctor is told which is which. Normally, the trial is ended only after a pre-determined number of volunteers have been recruited. At the end of the trial, the researchers count how many people got better in each of the two groups. If significantly more patients got better when they had taken the real pill than when they had taken the dummy, then the drug is deemed to have been proven. It is a brutally simple way to test pills, and the results are hard, dependable facts that medical insurance companies can rely on without fear of dispute. Humanistic treatments, such as hypnotherapy, fall into an exclusion zone, as they are not so easily put through the meat-grinder of the clinical trial. First there is no placebo. Second, it is hard to ensure uniformity of therapists if large numbers of patients are to participate in the trial. And it is only by using large numbers of patients that the play of chance can be made low enough for the effect of the treatment to be statistically clear. A factory can easily make ten thousand identical pills, but it is hard to find ten absolutely identical hypnotherapists. Third, a single pharmaceutical company can make large profits from sales of a single drug, and it can therefore afford to fund clinical trials. But no single organisation is going to reap rich rewards from establishing how good hypnotherapy is — so who is going to pay for trials of therapeutic hypnosis?

Yet, without published reports and research papers to guide them, medical insurance companies are reluctant to endorse what they see as unproven treatments. In the UK, PPP Healthcare reported in its brochure that:

"PPP Healthcare provides benefit for treatment (of their policyholders) according to a number of fundamental principles. Those principles state that, to be eligible for benefit, treatments should be of proven or widely accepted clinical effectiveness and should be given by appropriately qualified and registered clinical or medical professionals. The only non-medically qualified Clinical Practitioners (whose charges will be directly reimbursed) are practising members of certain professions allied to medicine. [These professions are recognised] for benefit purposes for outpatient services only under referral by a hospital specialist. The professions concerned are UKCC registered Nurses (specialising in stoma care, breast care, lymphatic drainage and psychotherapy), state registered dieticians, state registered orthoptists, speech therapists registered with the Royal College of Speech, and language therapists, psychologists, chartered physiotherapists and, psycho-therapists who are accredited membership of the British Association of Behavioural and Cognitive Psycho-therapists."

The cost of fees to cover a course of hypnotherapy sessions is paid for by the insurer only if the course is given by a clinical practitioner, and one who meets the criteria for registration in the above categories. Hypnotherapists are not recognised in their own right.

Norwich Union limit cover 'predominantly to the areas of osteopathy and chiropractic' reasoning that 'policies are designed to provide cover by medical and surgical specialists in a secondary care setting and this is mainly within the field of evidence-based mainstream medicine.' Optimistically, Norwich Union maintain, 'As clinical evidence for hypnotherapy becomes available, we will be reviewing this in the context of customer demand for complementary therapy and related activity elsewhere in the private medical insurance market.

British United Provident Association (BUPA) is an exception. Policies differ. Their comprehensive policies offer patients the benefits of hypnotherapy as a treatment to variable financial limits. To benefit, you must, of course, be a member of BUPA, and you must be subscribing to one of their more comprehensive policies. Furthermore, you must be referred for hypnotherapy by a BUPA registered consultant, and referred to a hypnotherapist holding a BUPA registration number. When all of these conditions are met, BUPA will pay your claims for hypnotherapy treatments within a prescribed budget.

In the UK, the Department of Health (DH) is also migrating from hostility, through ambivalence, toward acceptance of hypnotherapy. In the internal market under the auspices of regional National Health Service Trusts, the 'health service providers' — in other words, hospitals and general practitioners — have budgets to purchase services from independent providers in a range of alternative fields. These independents can and do include hypnotherapists. Each such independent provider is assigned a unique 'provider code', which makes it possible for an NHS doctor to purchase that provider's services for the benefit of the patients. This is a five-digit reference code that makes a therapist visible to the medical bureaucracy for payment purposes. Assignment of a provider code makes no judgement whatsoever as to the skill of the practitioner to whom the code is assigned by the Department of Health. Provider code details are copied to the local health authority and held within a directory of providers, categorised under individual home health authorities. Public access is available on the internet. Referral by your doctor or consultant would suffice as the best possible reference testifying to the standards and effectiveness of the hypnotherapy services offered. The door into the NHS is thus opened to hypnotherapists, but they are not necessarily invited in!

The Department of Health ultimately delegates to the individual authorities. Discussions then take place between the NHS Trust, the medical providers and the Primary Care Groups, who decide the policy. These three, together, look at the authority's population of patients and then make an assessment as to whether or not to offer a treatment more widely. The decision is also driven, of course, by the availability of funding. In theory, doctors are at liberty to provide any treatment whatsoever. But their choices may ultimately be driven by broad-brush selections and decisions at commissioning level, particularly those of the primary care groups.

The Department of Health produces an information booklet entitled *Complementary Medicine*, which gives information about various individual sorts of complementary therapy. The intended audience comprises the primary care groups. The main therapies included are acupuncture, aromatherapy, chiropractic, homeopathy, osteopathy, and hypnotherapy. Other therapies are included in lesser detail in the appendix of the same publication. The definition that is given in this publication describes the process of direct suggestion hypnosis, rather than interactive hypnotherapy. And it states that 'the primary use of hypnosis is in: anxiety, and disorders with a strong psychological component such as asthma and irritable bowel syndrome (and) conditions that can be modulated by levels of arousal such as pain.' Thus the more effective form of hypnotherapy is omitted, and the wide range of conditions that it can help, is passed over.

It is probable that, when Freud publicly distanced himself from hypnosis — and denied the efficacy of it — his words, words spoken by the 'father of psychoanalysis' stuck, and for the most part have continued to stick.

It is fair to say that when patients personally suggest the idea of hypnotherapy to their doctor, rarely have I heard of them being subsequently dissuaded from following a course of hypnotherapy sessions. But the initiative is rarely taken by the general practitioner. The Practice Nurse is more likely to suggest an alternative to a chemical formulation, and to be able to advise on the generic compound for a patient to buy, rather than the marketed and advertised 'brand'.

With the advent of Zyban, there is a drug to help stop smoking and so an ideal opportunity to direct patients towards an alternative is effectively lost to a chemical — a drug that has been fatal to some of those who sought it out to help them stop smoking. By contrast, hypnotherapy is drug-free.

A scientific report in 1992 cited both hypnotherapy and acupuncture as the two most effective ways to stop smoking. Journalist Robert Matthews interviewed the highly respected Oxford epidemiologist Sir Richard Doll, who first discovered that smoking causes lung cancer: Sir Richard said that the success of hypnosis "backed his own observations" and he contrasted it with "the low success rate of those who resorted to willpower alone" (New Scientist, 31st October 1992). Matthews also quoted Christopher Pattinson, academic chairman of the British Society of Medical & Dental Hypnosis: "The latest relaxation techniques achieve success rates of up to sixty per cent from a single session, he said". Since then, hypnotherapy has taken a large leap forward with interactive techniques, which have raised the success rate much higher.

8

◎

A QUESTION OF CONTROL
Who's controlling whom in hypnosis?

◎ "I will be really surprised if I can be hypnotised. I seem to have an over active conscious part — I cannot be really, really relaxed."

◎ "I felt I was battling against it."

◎ "When you are hypnotised, are you knocked out?"

◎ "If I hear a certain word — am I going to do silly things?"

◎ "I don't want to be made to do something against my will."

The techniques for helping someone into hypnosis can be learned by anyone adopting a responsible and caring approach. The most important focus in the context of one-to-one hypnotherapy, is what a skilled and creative practitioner can do therapeutically with hypnosis once the client is in the altered state of hypnosis. There is a plethora of books covering self-hypnosis and these generally include a so-called progressive induction (often quite lengthy) to help yourself or another into a relaxed state. Yes — a relaxed state. Hypnosis is a state of relaxation. There are light levels of relaxation and deeper levels of relaxation. As we saw earlier, in Chapter 4, we go in and out of trance-like states, which are very much like hypnosis, throughout our daily lives. Daydreaming induces a light state of hypnosis. Reading too, indices a light, trance-like state. When hypnosis is used to induce a state of anaesthesia for the purpose of performing surgery free of anaesthetics, that state is much, much deeper. At such a deep level you can less freely and easily speak, or use any movement even to indicate a 'Yes' or a 'No' response. For the purposes of interactive hypnosis you do need to be able to participate freely, easily and effortlessly. The light trance state (sometimes called the 'alpha' state, as it is associated with alpha brain waves) allows for this. At this level, you may speak, although perhaps only in whispers. Occasionally you may not wish to speak — or to verbalise any experience at all. Therefore, you can move your fingers to indicate a 'Yes', a 'No', or a 'I do not choose to answer that' response. These are called 'ideomotor' responses. You may scratch to relieve an itch on your face. You can laugh and you can cry in hypnosis. Neither laughing nor crying will necessarily disturb the trance state. I have observed a client open their eyes, and remaining in 'waking hypnosis', reach over for the glass of water, on my desk, drink to relieve a niggling cough, and then resume the relaxed state — again closing their eyes.

It is fair to say that in the initial session, your level of relaxation may be lighter than in subsequent sessions, because this is a new experience for you. Relaxing into hypnosis is an easy and effortless process. You do not have to work at it — so over-eagerness 'to go into' hypnosis can create unnecessary pressure. You are discovering the truth about hypnotherapy, a truth that is often different from what you previously had been led to believe by television and by stage hypnosis. Bear in mind that you are meeting your hypnotherapist for the first time, visiting a new environment, finding your way there and so on. You are likely to find that subsequent sessions of hypnosis will be more effective in deepening your level of relaxation simply because you know so much more about the practitioner and the situation.

Whatever your level of relaxation at the start you will find that you are likely to go deeper as each session progresses. And, like learning to ride a bicycle, once you have learnt, you generally do not forget how to ride it. When, in the future, you consider undergoing hypnotherapy to help you overcome some other problem, then, on the basis of previous success, you will find that you go deeper naturally. The state of hypnosis is now familiar and more accessible.

Taking yourself deeper into hypnosis, like going deeper into meditation, takes practice — and it takes more practice for some people than it does for others. The practice is often focused on learning to relax. To practice relaxing you do need to give yourself permission to relax and to allow time to do so. Listening to relaxation scripts on audio media definitely helps. Although many of the audio resources may not introduce the term 'hypnosis', in fact anything that relaxes you from the top of your head to the tips of your toes, or vice versa, leads you gently along and down the path into a relaxed trance-like state akin to hypnosis. If you sense that you are someone who really resists relaxation, then before visiting a hypnotherapist take the time to practice relaxing. The time invested will be well worth it, and will contribute to your success during the sessions.

> "When I'm 'there', I'm not wholly convinced. Part of me is on the outside looking in. I'm always very conscious of what I'm saying."

Hypnosis is an altered state of awareness, and specifically a heightened state of awareness. Awareness is the key. You are very much aware that you are in the hypnotherapist's room. You are aware of cars travelling down the road. You are aware of any background sounds such as a fountain, a dog barking, and these will not distract you. Your therapist may even suggest that all outside sounds aid and guide you into deeper levels of relaxation.

> "I'm a very analytical person, and am always trying to work things out. I'm always one step ahead of the game — always needing the right answer. I still feel an element of choice, and because I have to make a choice, I want to make the best choice."

Hypnosis is not a test. There are no right or wrong answers. You are under no compulsion to come up with anything. An interactive hypnotherapist will work with anything and she will also work with nothing. So, if nothing comes forward, say the word 'nothing', 'I don't know', 'blank' or 'pass'. There is always another way, another approach. There is always another question — a more effective question the therapist can ask. You do not need to lie there in the chair thinking 'It's not working', or 'It's not going to work for me.' And the natural curiosity of the mind is such that it will more than likely come up with something in answer to one of the approaches.

Hypnosis is a state of presence. In particular it is a *presence of mind* — as opposed to an absence of mind. Quite literally you give yourself the *present of presence*. You will be aware of, and you will remember the gist of what you say, and the gist, of what your hypnotherapist says. It is natural, helpful and enormously clarifying for this to happen.

"My big worry is — what if I cannot maintain it?"

The work does not stop when you leave the hypnotherapist's room — your subconscious may continue to give you more insight, more connections, and more growth. Remember too, the changes are going to continue to happen between sessions.

"I don't really know how, or why but yes, I felt it straight away. I felt like I wanted to put on different clothes — more confident clothes — to show people I'm more confident. It was like — I'm fine. I don't have to hide behind anything."

"I really had a change. [At a university panel interview.] There were ten people. Talking to the boss across the table, I really felt good. I was more confident to speak. I didn't feel any fear."

"Everyday I noticed the difference in things that I was doing. Just amazing!"

"The blushing is still there, but I have felt so much more relaxed. I have not been talking down to myself. I have generally been a lot lighter. I cannot believe I've noticed the difference so quickly. Incredible."

"I understand a bit more. I can see the pattern repeating itself. Negativity. It has brought up a lot of negativity. I'm not in a healthy relationship. I destroy, rather than protect myself."

Once you begin to re-orientate yourself, to experience yourself differently, and to understand yourself differently, the impact can start immediately. This may at first be only a subtle change, it might occur only at the level of your thinking: it might manifest as a modification of your habits of thought. But it will get bigger and bigger. Each situation or experience that now has a positive outcome and clarifies further your insights stacks up the evidence confirming your success in the hypnotherapy. The process of emotional re-education has begun. Evidence to the effect that you can be, and act, differently — sometimes immediately, and sometimes in time. Sometimes it takes a little more time.

"I wanted to test it out. The next morning my bosses were fighting and I was calmer about it. Later that week I had to facilitate one of the team meetings, and it went great."

You *can* speak up in meetings and interviews. You *can* be proud of your natural manicured professional-looking nails. Blushing occurs much less often, and if it happens at all, is perceived as a normal occurrence — and part of the human condition. Your confidence, self-esteem, and self-assurance grows and grows. Celebrating the difference supports and feeds success more and more. You do not deny the evidence, because it is your heart's desire. It is what you truly want. And because you have effectively designed and installed new mental 'software', the new version of events continues to run day after day — week after week — month after month. You do not revert back to the old software. The new software resides within your inner mind and plays full out. Confidence conquers fear. Confidence grows and grows — exactly as Confidence created and installed the software to run. In subsequent sessions of hypnotherapy you may install new versions on the same theme, ensuring you are glitch-free. You may iron out any glitches and fine tune the content of the suggestions for change. You may turn up the volume — taking time to thank your subconscious for doing such an amazing job. Enjoy declaring your success. You encourage and help ensure that your 'inner garden' of confidence does indeed continue to grow and grow and grow. Wonderful words offer the most nutritious form of diet for the mind.

Interactive hypnotherapy is a process of negotiation and persuasion. You are choosing what is to be jettisoned from your mind — and what is to stay — and what is to be cultivated and created, for harvesting in the here and now. It is not an experience of forcibly persuading or of bullying aspects of the inner mind into co-operating, nor is it an experience of compliance with the therapist — nor, for that matter, surprisingly, of compliance with you the client. Your subconscious can say 'no', especially when potentially vulnerable aspects of the inner mind come into play — aspects such as Fear, or Scared, particularly when a person has not experienced much of the quality that he or she is desirous of awakening — such as Faith.

'What', you might be asked, 'do you need more of, in order to allow Fear to come forward and speak?' The answers vary. Generally, responses include: more safety, more protection; and more love. Safety, Protection, or Love will be asked to come forward to offer that back up. With a committed sense of support in place aspects such as Doubt, Fear and Scared more readily and more comfortably step forward. All of the aspects must be in easy and comfortable agreement, just as the parties to a contract must arrive at a consensus, so it is with all the aspects of the mind. Every concerned aspect signs a metaphorical contract — a contract committing completely and absolutely to support you.

If you were to intuit any sense of discomfort, or coercion, then you would most likely end the trance state. If any form of words or ideas were to be introduced that were contrary to your morals, your values, beliefs, and culture — be they issues of faith or otherwise — then you may well open your eyes, effectively leaving the trance state. In other words, you will not do, or act in any way that is contrary to what you would be disposed to do in full conscious awareness.

Knowing and remembering the essential detail of what happens during each and every session keeps you in touch with your experience and keeps you in control. You remain grounded, and you remain, and continue to remain, empowered. You have more understanding, and with that increased understanding you have more clarity. The inner strengthening that you experienced in hypnosis grows. Then the good feelings build, having a fast and cumulative effect. Success builds success.

The reason that people who have experienced stage hypnosis do not appear to remember what happened to them is that the stage hypnotist embedded a specific command to that effect. This is called a post-hypnotic suggestion because it takes effect after the subject leaves the hypnotic trance. The stage subject may have rendered a fine performance of whatever was prescribed — impersonating an animal or a famous person, say — but cannot remember how they fared. Being greeted by laughing, jovial friends, teasing and cajoling their exploits may create problems. Unable to remember the truth of what happened, the stage subject may experience self-doubt, disempowerment, possible disorientation, displacement, and potentially a crisis of confidence. These side effects underline the importance of enabling the client to retain full recollection of what happens in hypnotherapy.

The changes in interactive hypnotherapy can come so quickly, and the transformation can be so effortlessly fast, that it would be bewildering for the client not to be aware of what happened. This is the reason I continue to say "It isn't magic, but it is magical!" You can gain a much clearer perspective on events and circumstances in the past from the hypnotherapy session, so setting you free to move forward. Hypnosis, be it one-to-one, together with a therapist or self-hypnosis in a solo situation, is a way of logging-in to yourself, as opposed to logging-out. It allows you to log into, and effectively gain access to, a deeper wisdom. This may sound mysterious, but really it is simply an internal state of your own knowledge and understanding, untrammelled by distractions. I would suggest that this inner place of wisdom can be accessed by practised meditators and by people who are practised at prayer. Hypnosis is a fast-track route to arrive at a similar place of peace and grace. One may argue that a person meditating and a person praying are doing different things — but the point is, the self-encounter is much the same.

Therapeutic hypnosis is a way of gaining control, not a way of absenting control. In hypnotherapy you gain access to the inner engine of your subconscious — in effect, having the opportunity to lift the bonnet of your personal engine and do some fine-tuning. Afterwards, you get to sit in the driving seat and to take control of something that may have been controlling, and indeed, 'driving' you. You get to access the controls, having now tuned the engine to eliminate the glitches and defects, and also having gained insights into how the engine works. The ability to put a stop to unwanted behaviours and habits such as smoking or nail biting falls out as an easy consequence of that interior access to the subconscious. With interactive hypnosis the hypnotherapist knows the procedures for tuning your internal mental engine — how to help you stop, revise, or transform the behaviour or habit — but the suggestions for change come from within you. You jettison the low-octane fuel that has driven the habit, and then re-fuel with high-octane suggestions for change.

The approach is one that may be termed 'permissive', and 'co-operative'. Christine Kirtley, in *Consumer Guide to Hypnosis* defines the permissive and co-operative way thus: '... the client has a more important role and the therapist is supportive, creating and maintaining a caring environment. The client is accepted as having the most knowledge of his own behaviour, the focus of work helping the client understand his experiences and use his energies and resources effectively.'

It is like Zen and the art of mental engine maintenance! It is as if you become your own guru — saving you the cost of a flight to India, Nepal, or Sedona.

9

SURRENDERING SCEPTICISM
Is hypnosis genuinely real?

The experience of hypnosis, however carefully and thoroughly explained, almost always prompts a series of questions about the authenticity of the clients' personal experience. Often, the client acknowledges that hypnosis works for others, but wonders, 'Will it really work for me?' A client can be whispering their subconscious responses in soft tones, and still they will say as they open their eyes at the end of the initial session, "I was very relaxed, but was I really hypnotised?"

Other comments along the same lines are these:

"I didn't notice any difference."

"I knew I was here in this room."

"It's an odd sensation. You are conscious the whole time."

"I knew exactly what was happening at every stage."

"I could have opened my eyes."

"I felt out of it, but I was aware of everything you were saying".

"I was able to think other thoughts."

"I couldn't concentrate on what you were saying."

"Nothing came into my mind."

"I felt something, but I resisted it."

"When I'm 'there', I'm not wholly convinced. Part of me is on the outside looking in. I'm always very conscious of what I'm saying."

The state of hypnosis is an altered state of awareness. It is not a state of sleep. Hypnosis is a way to reach a delicious state of relaxation, a state in which time passes very quickly. You may find it quite incredible to learn that you have been in this relaxed state for almost an hour or more. An hour in hypnosis is, in a sense, equivalent to a couple of hours of sleep, in so far as one awakens from the relaxation feeling rested, rejuvenated and mentally cleansed. Certainly, clients often report feeling lighter, after dissolving and eliminating whatever energy-eating emotion they had come to deal with.

Hypnosis is not a passive state. You can laugh in hypnosis, and you can cry in hypnosis. Neither emotion will necessarily disturb the state of relaxation. If, however, you were to be faced with some form of danger — if, say, someone outside the practice room were to shout "Fire!" then you, the client, would immediately end the hypnotic state. Of course your hypnotherapist would intervene to bring you out anyway, but she wouldn't need to. Your natural protective faculties would bring you back into the room, fully back into full waking consciousness.

"When you were putting me under, I didn't believe I was in hypnosis… until I just woke up".

As you've already learned, hypnosis is a voluntary state. To go into hypnosis you do need to concentrate and you do need to listen to the simple instructions. When you do not listen, you are quite right, you may not go into the deeply relaxing state, and you may remain in your normal state of mind. The instructions that make-up the Elman Induction — which I personally favour, and I included in Chapter 4 — are of a grammatically clumsy nature. The Elman script comprises words, that when spoken, in conjunction with the accompanying gestures, on the part of the hypnotherapist, introduce confusion, possibly between the left and the right sides of the brain. This confusion is what swiftly facilitates the deeply relaxing state. Any deepener that follows this procedure will achieve exactly that result — of deepening the state.

The mind is naturally curious and untamed prior to training. Meditators find their thoughts can wander away from the repetition of a word, or their focus from an image. During meditation, we can so easily become fascinated by something that happened during the day, or can whiz off to create a suddenly interesting shopping list. Eventually you realise that you have been distracted, and come back to continue to repeat the relaxing word, or to renew focus upon a chosen image. Likewise, in hypnosis, one can wander off on a reverie, then realise that that has happened, and return immediately to the issue being discussed. "What did you say?" or "Could you repeat that question?" are fairly regular responses.

It may take a bit longer to get someone into the hypnotic state if he is not very susceptible, but in the calm of the hypnotherapist's consulting room there is time to be persistent and work to achieve the required state — which is not possible on the stage in front of an audience hungry for results. Even those among you who describe yourselves as control freaks more often than not do actually go easily and effortlessly into hypnosis. Once you have got yourself to a hypnotherapist, you naturally want it to work, and hypnosis is a natural part of human experience. With the mind always protected by the subconscious, trance is — as we saw in Chapter 3 — a normal part of everyday life. If you are already proficient in its use, you will be able to enter and leave the state so easily you will hardly notice it. On the second session of hypnotherapy, you will be much more relaxed.

Be fair to yourself and consider that on your first session:

◎ You may be nervous — you're human. Nervousness is a healthy indication that you are alive!

◎ You may be convinced by what you have seen on television and on stage, and never thought you would go to such lengths.

◎ You really, really want it to work, but are resisting because there is a reluctance and fear of losing control.

◎ You want to get it right! Hypnotherapy is your last resort!

◎ You may be meeting your hypnotherapist and the environment for the first time.

◎   You have come from work, possibly leaving something pending, unfinished or urgent in the office, so;

◎   You may literally have other things on your mind.

◎   Your primary reason for going to see a hypnotherapist may be getting in the way. Anxiety would be a prime illustration.

◎   You simply need more practice at relaxation.

Bear in mind that on the second session, the journey and navigation are already familiar. You have seen the environment in which the therapy will take place. You will already know the truth about hypnotherapy, and you will have already met your therapist. Having got those first-visit concerns out of the way you are likely to be in a much more relaxed frame of mind.

You now know that it is an intuitive process, which requires a significant amount of spontaneous inspiration. It is not a rational process. Indeed it is very irrational. To your conscious mind there may initially seem no rhyme or reason at all for the words and phrases that come forward.

However sceptical, you do want to go into hypnosis and will generally be disappointed when nothing seems to happen.

This is so often perceived as failure — failure in the sense that you think you may have done something 'wrong', and personally failed the hypnosis 'test'. To redress the balance, please do be aware that there are a small percentage of subjects who do not go into hypnosis.

In Gillian Cross's children's book *The Demon Headmaster*, one of the young protagonists, Harvey, is hopeful that the new pupil in the hypnotically controlled school might be on their side — "another 'normal'." In the context of the book, 'normal' is a term used by Harvey to describe someone at the school who is not susceptible to hypnosis by their headmaster.

> 'Lloyd [his brother] looked at him scornfully. "Is it likely? I ask you! There's only five of us in the whole school. No, she'll be one of *them*."

There is a very small minority of people who do not go into hypnosis to some level or degree. Precisely how big is this portion? That is really unknown. For the sake of illustration, let us say a ballpark figure of five per cent.

An inability to relax on the initial session should not immediately classify you as falling into the 'five percent' margin. Be open to considering a second session and consider doing some relaxation practice before your return visit. Trance states do vary from light, to medium, to deep. Neither the medium nor the deep trance state is necessary to obtain definite benefits in hypnotherapy. Even a light trance is adequate to make a lot of progress.

Then there is always the option of considering another hypnotherapist. Having observed the normal courtesy of giving due notice of your intentions (forty-eight hours notice of cancellation is usual) — shop around. Hypnotherapy is a service. It is important to find a hypnotherapist offering a service that you feel comfortable with and that fits you well. Different therapists do employ different approaches, and another approach may well work for you.

I'm **afraid** of **hypnosis**   but I don't **know why**

10

◎

LIFTING THE VEIL

Hypnotherapy can reveal why things happen in your mind

Hypnotherapy has its natural home in the right-hand hemisphere of the brain. There may appear to be no logic in the words that come forward in hypnosis. Therefore, your left brain hemisphere can seem like a heckler objecting in the audience. "That doesn't make any sense!", "That cannot be right, it doesn't fit in with anything I know about!", "Well, I've never heard of that before!", "This is mumbo-jumbo!", "That can't be right, it doesn't follow any logic!", "You've lost the plot!", "Nonsense!", or just "Rubbish!". Interactive hypnotherapy is a spontaneous process, one that allows spontaneous invention and intuition to come to the fore, while the rigid hand of reason takes a short vacation. The self-censoring tendency, which demands that your thoughts must be what you expect them to be, relaxes and affords you a 'space' to think the unexpected. The suggestions, strategies and solutions that the subconscious presents are often inspiring, and indeed, thought-provoking to the conscious mind. Throughout daily life, words and phrases often just pop into the conscious mind, one by one, in odd moments of reverie — or moments of intuition. But if they fail to fit in with your predefined expectations, then they quickly find themselves in the dustbin of the mind. Hours, days, and sometimes weeks later, we can be cajoled into remembering the formerly disregarded thought-form, and reflect on how that thought, had we acted upon it, would have served us well. We are apt to say, 'if only I'd followed my intuition — my gut feeling'. What we can do in hypnosis is open the door for thoughts and images to travel between the conscious and subconscious more easily. The key to effective and successful hypnotherapy, rather than just hypnosis, is to marshal these thoughts and images so that they do something constructive instead of milling around aimlessly in your head. And the way we do that is to use *interactive* hypnotherapy — to engage thoughts and ideas in a dialogue about what they are about.

The whole of your brain is driven by patterns. The left brain specialises in regular, rule-governed patterns such as logic and language; and the right brain specialises in unsystematic, and hence less definable patterns. Patterns are discovered in echoes and resonances of thoughts, and shapes and forms emerge out of the hubbub. This is what the left-brain calls intuition, because they do not fit in with the explanations of the left, rational hemisphere of the brain. It goes under various labels: intuition; gut feeling; the inner voice; guidance; higher self; insight; divine intelligence; illumination; God. All of these may sometimes be classed by people at different times as 'psychic', meaning anything that is outside the physical realm. Only the right hemisphere of the brain can engage with the supposedly psychic awareness.

The whole of the mind operates by patterns. It works with layers of patterns, laid over one another — and only the top layer comes into conscious awareness. All of the other layers are kept submerged beneath the level of conscious awareness. Psychologists call this boundary the 'limen', and when things reach down through this liminal boundary, and affect the subconscious, they are called 'subliminal'. This is what happens when someone has a panic attack. You might observe something that in itself is innocuous, but because the pattern it follows happens to resonate with a pattern that is stored in the subconscious, it triggers an adverse reaction — be it a panic attack, stuttering, or morbid fear of any kind. That reaction seems to come from nowhere, because normally you cannot see through the liminal barrier. Hypnosis gives you access to those layers below the limen, and there you can find the pattern that is doing the mischief.

Let us take a typical example — an irrational fear of, say, lizards. To call it a fear of lizards is, in fact, an over-simplification of what is going on. The so-called fear of lizards is only the apparent symptom. What you are experiencing is not an actual fear of lizards, but a fear of the unconscious pattern that the lizard hooks into. So telling yourself that lizards are nothing to be afraid of will not do much good, as that is not what the fear is really about. The lizards are simply symbols, harmless creatures on the ground that happen to have acquired an association with something that really

did frighten you some time ago. What is happening is an unconscious connection with something embedded in a subliminal layer
of patterns. There is a stored pattern that the lizard is associated
with. That pattern might be grief. A very young girl sees a mini-
ature tragedy played out before her eyes: her grandmother's pet
cat catches, and eats, a lizard, and then dies from the poison in the
lizard. This is not something the child can forget. On the other
hand it is not something that the child can fully deal with: she
cannot integrate it into her world-view. As long as this strange
event is not integrated into her world-view, it stays around like a
nagging, distracting aggravation. So, as an act of self-protection,
the mind seals up that complex pattern of lizard, cat, and grief in
the subconscious. It becomes embedded in a subliminal layer, and
stays there for years and decades. Later, when the grown-up
woman sees a lizard running across the road, the conscious mind
has no particular reaction, as it knows that the lizard is not dangerous. In the subconscious layer, however, the image of the lizard
automatically registers with the stored pattern. The memory of
grief that is locked into the association with that lizard then floats
up like an echo through the limen into the conscious mind: and the
woman experiences a strange feeling of terror, as if from nowhere,
but somehow tied to the harmless lizard.

Case Study: Angela

Angela booked to come for interactive hypnotherapy, only a few
days prior to her departure to Greece. This transcript details her
initial session. The follow-up session, unusually a couple of days

later, focussed on further coaching and encouragement of her chosen team.

The interactive dialogue that follows is conversationally phrased in colloquial speech much as the real session, and therefore may at times not reflect the correct rules of grammar.

Angela talked, at the same time glancing though the window behind her, to check for any movement of the lizard-shaped leaves that could leap up and dance when caught up in the late English summer breeze.

A: I want to get rid of my phobia of lizards. The fact that they are around, scares me. They really can ruin my holiday. I'm going to Greece on Wednesday. I know there are a few around. The green ones are the ugliest — the colour of poison. The brown ones are less scary. Every single holiday I remember how many I see, and what each of them is like. They look like — ugh! — so ugly. I pretend I don't see them. As a teenager I could live with it, but it is getting worse. When I was in junior school, when we had to study the lizard, I got my mother to absent me from school ...

D: In a moment I will count from one to three, and click my fingers, and your subconscious will come forward in the form of a word or a picture. I will talk into that vision, and the answers that come forward will *be* your subconscious speaking. ... One. Two. Three... *[Fingers click gently. ...]* What word or picture comes forward?

A: A light

D: I will speak into that vision, and the answers that come forward will be your subconscious speaking.

D: You *are* Angela's subconscious, Yes or No? Pause. And it's fine if you're not too sure.

A: Yes

D: Thank you for coming forward, and thank you for monitoring Angela's being all of her life — for nurturing her most successful life. Subconscious, Angela reports to me that she is scared of lizards. Subconscious, may I ask respectfully, what is the reason for Angela being scared of lizards? … A word will come forward.

A: They are quite ugly.

D: Subconscious, knowing that you're very safe and *very* protected here in this room, would you allow Ugly to come forward and speak?

A: Yes.

D: On a count of three let Ugly come forward. One. Two. Three. *[Fingers click gently.]* Ugly, are you there? Yes or No?

A: Yes.

D: Thank you for coming forward. Ugly, may I ask, respectfully, for how long have you been resident in Angela's inner mind? Pause. Approximately?

A: For years and years and years.

D: Angela, in order to gain a sense of clarity and understanding and freedom from ugly in the here and now, would you agree to go back years and years and years, to the moment, the situation, or the circumstance when ugly *first* seeded itself in Angela's inner mind. Yes or No?

A: Yes.

D: Thank you. Know that you are very safe and very protected, here in this room. In a moment I will count from one to three, and tap your forehead, and you'll go back years and years and years ago, to the moment — the situation — the circumstance, Ugly first seeded within your inner mind. One. Two. Three. *[D taps A's forehead gently.]* shshshshshshsh... Where are you? ... Where do you sense you are?

A: I'm in the house. I'm two years old. My mum. My granny. They have a little cat, and the cat eats a lizard he has caught in the fields, and he dies. I'm shaking.

D: Little One, I'd like you to sense someone coming to join you, and your mum, and your granny, and there's no reason to be afraid or alarmed. Sense a young woman coming towards you Little One. She's smiling directly towards you, a very loving — unconditionally loving smile. And, as you look up, Little One you're really rather curious, because you realise this person looks kind of familiar — indeed this person looks very much like you — and you wonder how can this possibly be, because this person is a grown-up. As she gets closer Little One you realise this person is you — the person you grow up to be. And truly, Little One of *all* the people in the whole wide world this older you, knows *exactly* how you feel right now. Let her come and be beside you. Pause. Perhaps she gives you a big, *big* hug, and tells you how much she loves you, and how *very, very,* special you grow up to be. ... And know this grown-up you is very, very much on your side — on your team. ... Little One, can you believe, this grown-up-you has carried forward what happened today into her grown-up life? So much so, she has grown up very scared of lizards. Now Little One she would very much like to be free. ... Especially as she is going on holiday to a place where there are likely to be other lizards. Little One, would you agree to help her?

A: Yes.

D: To help *you*, you get the chance to invite a wise being — one whose wisdom you trust — one whose integrity you trust. Your chosen wise-being may be a friend or a relative, ... a character from a book, ... a favourite teddy bear, ... a pet, ... or a wise tree. Pause. Let your chosen wise-being come and *be* beside you right now. And say 'yes' when he or she is there.

A: Yes.

D: Perhaps they too give you a big, big, hug, and tell you how much they love you and how special you grow up to be. ... Know too that the wise being is very much on your side. ... Little One, knowing that *your* chosen wise being is right by your side — on your team, I'd like you to say what needs to be said to the grown-up you, and know that on this occasion the grown-up you *will listen* and *will hear* whatever you choose to share.

A: *[Little One to the Grown-up Angela.]* It's going to be okay. It's not going to be bad. It was only a small incident.

D: Let your wise being respond.

A: *[Wise being.]* My Grandfather says he is going to help me. He's quite big and even if I am shaking, he's not scared.

D: Grown-up Angela, having heard what you've heard and having learned what you've learned please speak to the Little One, and know that she *will listen* and *will hear* whatever you choose to say. Speak now and know the Little One is listening.

A: *[Grown-up to the Little Angela.]* I'm not scared.

D: And now let your Grandfather share his wisdom.

A: *[Wise being.]* He's going to buy me an ice cream.

D: Grown-up Angela, Little Angela, how does that begin to feel?

A: I'm a bit shaky

D: Do you feel comfortably shaky? Yes or No?

A: Relieved.

D: Little Angela, ... Grown-up Angela, I'd like you both to thank your wise being for sharing their loving wisdom, and know that your Grandfather can be with you, in a heartbeat, just by thinking of him.

A: *[Grown-up Angela, together with the Little Angela.]* Thank you. You were a great help.

D: Grown-up Angela, I'd like you please, to turn to the Little Angela. ... ... And say to the Little One, 'I promise, you will never have to experience this again. I love you, and I will always protect you.' ... ... And, hugging the Little Angela, sense yourselves merge shshshshshsh... Longer pause. In a moment, I will count from one to three and tap your forehead, and you'll come back to the here and now *remaining* in hypnosis. ... One, two, three. *[D taps A's forehead gently.]* shshshshshsh... Pause. Ugly, are you listening?

A: Yes.

D: Ugly, having learned what you've learned, and having experienced what you've experienced, may I ask respectfully, do you *truly* contribute anything of positive and advantageous benefit to Angela's life and well-being? ... Yes or No?

A: No.

D: Acknowledging that truth, would you agree now, to be dissolved and eliminated within Angela' inner mind? Yes or No?

A: Yes.

D: Thank you. ... Subconscious, are you listening?

A: Yes.

D: Subconscious, I'd like you please, to begin a very special mission, together with Angela's wise being if you wish. I'd like you to begin a search throughout Angela's subconscious mind and body — from the top of her head to the tips of her fingers and toes — to search though every organ, every tissue, and every cell of her being — to search for each and every feeling of Ugly — every sensation of Ugly — every thought form — every word — each and every memory allied to, and associated with Ugly — to search caringly and conscientiously throughout Angela's whole-being — to gather

Ugly together in its *entirety* in the form of a shape or an object. Take your time — take as long as it takes — and report what shape or object comes forward.

A: A vase.

D: Be curious to notice what the vase is made of.

A: Made of clay.

D: Subconscious, I'd like you please to do whatever it takes to eliminate this vase made of clay, together with the help of your Grandfather, if you wish — to eliminate it completely and absolutely — and to report what you've done.

A: Smashed it with a hammer.

D: Please remove the clay fragments completely and absolutely, and report what you've done. Pause. Report when there is no trace — no trace whatsoever.

A: Gone. Swept away.

D: Thank you subconscious. ... Subconscious, how does that feel?

A: I'm running in the fields. It's nice and hot.

D: What needs to be in place for Angela to feel even freer to run in the fields?

A: Determination.

D: Would you allow Determination to come forward and speak? Yes or No?

A: Yes.

D: On a count of three, let Determination come forward. One. Two. Three. *[D clicks fingers to coincide with 'shshshshshsh...'.]* Shshshshshsh... Determination, are you there?

A: Yes.

D: Welcome. Determination, you are truly pivotal to Angela experiencing a sense of freedom to run in the fields, day after day after day. Determination, will you agree to support Angela?

A: Yes.

D: Wonderful. I'd like you please, to share all of the many, many ways you *now* intend to support Angela. Share whatever bright ideas and loving suggestions pop into mind.

A: *[Determination.]* After I've been to Greece — I'm determined — I want to go to Morocco.

D: Determination, are you now ready to embed that intention in Angela's inner mind? Yes or No?

A: Yes.

D: Determination, I'd like you to embed that intention as an absolute command — an absolute commitment to Angela — deep, deep, deeply down, in the very foundation of her inner mind. Take as long as it takes, and say 'yes' when you've done.

A: Done.

D: Determination, is there a companion within Angela's inner mind, a team player, whom you would like to come forward to support you — to play full out alongside you — to help champion Angela's success?

A: Yes.

D: What name does that companion go by?

A: There's a big tortoise-shell cat with long fluffy hair. It's Micky!

D: On a count of three, let Micky prance forward. *[Click of fingers. Louder celebratory voice.]* Micky, are you there?

A: Yes.

D: Thank you for prancing forward. Determination has chosen you to be a companion player on Angela's team. Please share how you <u>now</u> intend to be a championing presence by her side — on her team.

A: *[Micky.]* There will be no reason to be scared. I'm going to check there are no vicious creatures around. I'm going to check the balconies. I'm going to play with the lizards and push them away. I'm going to support Determination.

D: Micky I'd like you to embed those wise ideas and suggestions, as absolute commands — absolute commitments — deep, deep, deeply down alongside those of Determination, in the very foundations of Angela's inner mind. Take as long as it takes, and say 'yes' when you've done.

A: Done.

D: Subconscious how does that feel?

A: Feels relaxed.

D: Subconscious do you have any objections to Angela feeling more and more relaxed and free? Yes or No?

A: No.

D: Subconscious will you agree to work together with Determination and Micky, to ensure this work now goes ahead properly, correctly, and permanently?

A: Yes.

D: Fantastic. And how long will it be now before Angela notices a difference? Will it be some time, or will it be *immediately*?

A: Now.

D: That's great.   Subconscious, I'd like you please to bring forward, a picture, or a sense of a picture of a ten-metre-high movie screen, and tell me when you have it — or a sense of it.

A: Yes, I have it.

D: And on to that screen I'd like you to project, a picture, or a sense of a picture of Angela exactly as she now chooses to be. A picture of Angela on holiday in Greece experiencing herself relaxed, determined and free. Pause. And how does that picture of Angela look?

A: It's a picture of me relaxing on a balcony together with Micky. I'm happy. He's playing with the lizards and pushing them away.

D: This picture can look happy, and happier, free and freer. At the bottom of this screen are three buttons or dials. The button on the far left allows you to fine tune the clarity of this picture — to turn up the brightness — to adjust minor details. And the button in the middle allows you to turn up the volume on the stronger and stronger sense of Determination, the sense of freedom, and sense of happiness as you relax more and more, knowing Micky is taking care of them. And the button on the far right, allows you to turn up the volume on what you're saying inside your head as you realise *your* success, and what Micky is saying as he acknowledges *your* success. Spend a few moments adjusting those buttons — until the picture is, *exactly* as you *now* choose it to be. Take as long as you wish, and say 'yes', when it's absolutely perfect. *[A period of silence allows time for fine-tuning and adjustment.]*

A: Yes

D: And how's that picture looking now?

A: I'm sensing the green ones and the brown ones, but Micky takes care of them. I'm okay. I'm relaxed.

D: *Now* sense yourself walking towards that screen — stepping into the screen — experiencing that joy — breathing in the sense of freedom, feeling happy and happier, and more and more relaxed, knowing they're being taken care of — experiencing yourself together with Micky, exactly as you *now* choose to be. And how's that picture looking now?

A: A different attitude. I'm climbing. There are rocks and flowers and I have a nice bag and a ponytail. It's hot. The birds are singing.

D: Having learned what you've learned, and having experienced what you've experienced, sense yourself stepping forward — maybe to Wednesday — with a sense of Determination and Micky playing right by your side — *on your team* — sense yourself in a situation that may have triggered your old behaviour — and be curious to notice what's happening now and how Angela appears to be. Pause. And report what is happening.

A: I'm walking to the flat. Nice flowers.

D: Now take yourself forward — maybe seven days from now — into another situation that may have triggered your behaviour, and report what happens.

A: There's a lizard in the background — on the balcony. It is small with black eyes, and a bit smiley. Micky plays with it and pushes it away.

D: Take yourself forward ten to fourteen days from now, and report how Angela *now* appears to be.

A: She's happy. There are no lizards. I'm okay.

D: And celebrate your success. Take a few moments to truly, truly thank Determination and Micky for playing full out on your team — and to thank your subconscious, for the extra-ordinary work it has done on your behalf this morning — pointing out all of the advantages and all of the benefits, you have gained and will continue to gain, as this work now goes ahead, properly, correctly and permanently. Take as long as you wish, and say 'yes' when you've done.

A: Yes.

D: In a moment I will count from ten to one. And on the count of one you will open your eyes — sensing Determination *strong* and *stronger* right by your side, and Micky playing very close by. Ten, nine, eight: coming up now. Determination deter-mined to go to Morocco. Seven: sensing Micky playing, taking very good care, now — right by your side. Six: feeling relaxed. Five: more and more happy day by day — determined, relaxed, happy and happier. Four: *for* your entire life. Three: *free* and freer. Two: more and more alert — more and more awake. One: eyes open, fully aware, fully alert. Full waking consciousness! Slowly and gently coming back into the room, wriggling your fingers and toes — and celebrate.

The case of the lizard phobia illustrates how associative memory works in the brain: when one part of the pattern comes to the notice of the mind (e.g. the mind notices a lizard), then the other part is also immediately evoked (e.g. the fear erupts into the mind). And so the person feels fear and doesn't understand what the fear is about: the rational mind says, "This is only a lizard — what is there to be afraid of?"

It is important to notice that the underlying mechanism is that of matching patterns. The unconscious mind just sees certain specific things and is triggered to act in a certain way. It acts very simply. Whereas other therapies tend towards looking for elaborate plots to interpret the stories, the truth is that the subconscious is quite dumb.

In general terms, there are two ways of explaining why something goes wrong — a conspiracy theory or a mistake theory. Freudian analysis would come up with a conspiracy theory, that the subconscious is deliberately conspiring to produce fear because of its own agenda, which is probably sexual. In fact, what has happened is a mistake. At some point, the subconscious mind has made a mistake and is reacting to the lizard in a way that is inappropriate.

As we noted earlier, the mind is always looking for patterns — it is continually bombarded by different stimuli and it craves order. The mind is always striving to bring things forward as a pattern. If a child experiences a trauma — an extraordinary event — then the child cannot fit that into the pattern of events she has experienced thus far in life, and so when she has one of these events (seeing the cat die, for instance) the child does not know how to fit it into her view of the world. If this memory stayed in conscious awareness, the mind would repeatedly become occupied in trying to integrate it into the pattern it sees in the world. As a self-defence against that obsession, however, it is stored as a subconscious memory. There is thus a natural defence mechanism in the mind to render the memory unconscious. When the memory is made *un*conscious, by being repressed inside the *sub*conscious mind, then the conscious mind is free to get on with its life without being irritated by this memory.

Later on, the mind has matured, and has acquired a richer world-view. The matured mind can make sense of a more complex world. It has a wider and more nuanced repertoire of concepts to deal with what happens in the world. Death is an example of this. You now know that life comes and life goes, and that you can integrate this into the bigger pattern. A child may not possess that comprehension. And, when unexpectedly confronted by sudden death, the child cannot integrate that event into her world-view and stashes it away in the subconscious — where it remains even after the growing person has acquired an understanding of death.

So in hypnosis, by bringing that subconscious memory back into conscious awareness you give the conscious mind a fresh opportunity to integrate it. Now, because of the maturation of the mind, and because of the mind's richer resources it is able to accomplish that integration. So when the person subsequently sees the lizard — or whatever used to trigger the problem — that memory still responds exactly as before, but now because the memory is conscious, that person can see exactly where the memory is coming from. When she now sees a lizard, and recalls a memory of grief, she knows it is about the cat dying and so it is not a problem. She can handle it, knowing it was a notion of death, of fear, and now it is linked to something limited — the cat's death. Bringing past experience into consciousness is often sufficient to heal it.

By bringing the adult to the child, you effectively disempower the pattern and empower the child.

The following simple analogy might help to illustrate this model. Imagine someone working in a kitchen she's not familiar with, and an alarm goes off. This person does not know what the alarm is about. It may be the fire alarm. It may not. On enquiry she is told that it is just the oven and it merely signals that the cooking is finished. So then she can handle it. Anxiety attacks work in a similar way: a sense of alarm arises, but the individual does not know what it is about, so it is deeply disturbing. When the origins of the alarm are known consciously, it is no longer disturbing, or much less so.

Accessing the child is a way of managing and speeding up the healing.

Time Travel Mirror
A child asked what the future held
As the child walked away
I recognised the child
But it was too late
Now as an adult
I wish I knew myself

J. Alastair Howarth

We can unconsciously accept suggestions that we don't even know we've accepted. In childhood you're often told things in a coercive way, so the child stores the memory that if it doesn't do something it may be hurt.

Advertisers know the unconscious layers of patterns that people respond to. As long as the patterns lie half-buried in the subconscious, no amount of willpower will disarm the automatic responses that they engender.

A recent campaign of adverts for flowers played on this very acutely. The campaign was aimed at men. One of the copy-lines was: "The last time Tom bought flowers for his wife he was wolf-whistled by some building workers." This taps into the now-latent shame that, as an infant, he was made to feel when he did girlish things when he was being socialised as a boy. It has not gone away. It is still there, still potent, and the advertisers earn their keep by knowing where to probe to activate these hidden reservoirs of fear and anxiety. Most of the advertisements you see are not intended for you. They are for someone else. You are lulled into a false sense of security regarding advertisements if you think that you are unaffected by any of them. You are unaffected by the ones that don't target you. Then they slip one in, which is aimed right at your unconscious fear of shame, and you react without knowing what's driving your reaction. You are acting upon that unconscious layer in your mind.

Nature is very simple, and very economical. The mind is a great abstracter, and handles analogies and metaphors as easily as the heart beats or the lungs breathe. For example, a gap in your life symbolically matches an empty feeling in your stomach. So you stuff yourself with food to end the endless craving. But it doesn't go away because it fails to address what the feeling was really all about in the first place. If you had an awareness of where this empty feeling was coming from, you would not possess this need to over-eat in a vain attempt to fill the gap.

Where psychological problems have come from is often very simple. Something bad happened in childhood or adolescence and you're half-remembering it. This is the reason why hypnotherapy can be so effective so quickly. Your subconscious mind is not waging a conspiracy against you. It is actually very dumb, and has got its wires crossed. If we were dealing with complicated malfunctions of the mind, we could not fix things in three to five sessions of hypnotherapy. Each and every session is complete in itself, comprising a beginning, a middle, and a generally happy and liberating end. And miracles do happen.

Sometimes one session is all it takes. The outcome can be gradual incremental change to instant transformation.

Surprises are rare in hypnosis. The subconscious mind will provide information as and when you are ready to receive it. On an initial session clients may say emphatically, there are certain areas of their lives where they *do not want to go* — the death of a parent at a young age, say. Tessa held this view, and a view of herself that she was 'not good enough', a thought form that had been embedded a long time ago. As she had chosen consciously 'not to go there', her subconscious gave her *a different point of view*. "I'm in my first year at school. It is time to leave. My mum isn't there. I am the only one there waiting. She's not come to collect me."

This event was not the one Tessa had anticipated meeting up with, and one her adult self did not warrant as that significant at all. Your subconscious mind will give you that 'information' and 'clarity' you are ready to receive. In a sense her subconscious had taken full account of her conscious wishes. Moreover, to the sensitive younger self, seeing things through the child's eyes, the event may naturally have held more emotional significance. Therein lies a whole layer of private poignancy. Tessa began to understand. Young Tessa was able to recover and re-join the memory of her mum dashing in great haste to meet her — anxious, loving and apologetic. Her younger self felt the love and the presence of the reunion, and the reassurance of her mum's commitment to be with her. The seeds of value, worth, and love were sewn. In a subsequent session, these seeds, nourished by Confidence and Self-Love, grew into sunflowers, standing tall and taller by her side.

So often is the case that clients say incredulously "So that's what it was about!" realising the event was often altogether 'less traumatic' than they had consciously envisaged and discussed. The events that have influenced our feelings and our inter-pretations about ourselves are often events and situations that we knew about, or remembered in hypnosis, when our memories were jogged. What we did not know, is how those events and situations were fuelling our experience of ourselves in our present lives — in the here and now. We did not know the emotional charge that the infant mind attached to those memories. Reflecting at the end of a one and only session, Barbara said, "When I was sitting on mum's lap I kept crying and crying in the hope that mum would have him [her father] back. I can't believe that it's that incident – from that moment. I thought it was something I was blocking. I thought it would be more complicat-ed. I feel so much more relaxed." In hypnosis, you can first discover the source of the flow of emotionally confusing and sometimes disabling mental fuel. Then, through discussion and negotiation in hypnosis, you can drain low-grade fuel away at source, after which you can re-discover and re-activate reserves of fresh high-grade fuel to pump through a positive life-line for continuous good in the here and now.

The 'crossing of wires' is particularly common in the case of phobias, when what is fuelling the phobia is not necessarily an event to do with the subject of the phobia. A fear of flying is not necessarily fuelled by a flying mishap or anything else directly relevant to the dangers of flying. Sam, aged nineteen, was taking a night flight back from a holiday in Boston with her boyfriend Steve. She couldn't sleep. Worry, guilt, sadness, and regret filled up the confined space around her. Her mind was crammed with fear. Her body was restless, tense and uncomfortable. On stepping from the plane, Sam had an appointment with fear — an appointment to terminate her pregnancy. This was the real fear — one that Sam had wrestled with for the duration of that seemingly endless flight.

Nor is fear of an animal or an insect, necessarily fuelled by an unhappy encounter with that kind of animal or insect. Rather, the fuel may be a juxtaposed situation around the object of our fear. When you have a fear, you certainly know about it, and you become an expert in it.

What you generally do not know is why you have the fear in the first place. The fear is so often a fear of the unknown. The rational mind can state quite categorically "the fear is silly", but that doesn't magic it away. Why you have it, when there is a relevant why, is often related to, but different from the subject of the fear. Simply, the object of the fear — of flying, of creatures, or whatever — gets caught up in a one-off situation, and keeps you in the dark. In hypnosis, you are guided and supported to unravel the crossed wires and to correctly place the respective plugs into the correct sockets. You then have immediate relief and more regular functioning. The freedom from the fear is often immediate and permanently re-wired into the subconscious.

Interactive hypnosis is an explorative and spontaneous process. Words and phrases pop into mind. Some bring clarity and understanding, some may surprise, and some will intrigue.

Recently I worked with a number of women to free them from the common problem of 'blushing', 'flushing', or plain 'going bright red'. Blushing I discovered is a much more common problem than many people realise, and many 'just put up with it'. One client told me that her doctor simply advised 'more concealer!'. Many of the women had gone through the counselling route before coming to me. But, because counselling did not access the root, the problem persisted. In all cases the blushing was getting worse and particularly so at work. Some people are so desperate that they will spend thousands of pounds on a surgical operation to try to stop the blushing. This involves severing or blocking a nerve (in sympathicotomy) or removing a nerve ganglion (sympathectomy) in the neck that is the immediate cause of blushing. This nervous tissue is part of the 'sympathetic', or automatic, nervous system, hence the name of the operation. The operation has existed since the 1920s, but has entered the cosmetic surgery market in recent years through the use of keyhole surgery allowing a tiny endoscope to be inserted through a very small incision away from the neck. This is commonly referred to as

Endscopic Transthoracic Sympathectomy (ETS). It has been used on thousands of patients around the world, but was publicised as a 'new' treatment in London last year by Mr Anthony Mitra at the Highgate Private Hospital, even though, for example, Mr Alan Cameron has been doing it in Ipswich since 1984. As with any surgical intervention, there is a certain proportion of side effects, and with some patients the operation fails to achieve the required result, or succeeds only temporarily. In fact, the rate of adverse side effects is so great, that the earlier operation of cutting the nerve has been replaced by merely clamping the nerve, so that the operation can be reversed (at further cost) if necessary.

The existence of this operation was interesting because in about ninety per cent of the cases I have had, there was an emotional root. This is thus one more example of the creeping medicalisation of normal human problems. What is more interesting is the lack of objective assessment of the operation. Part of the brand image of 'medical' treatments is that they are scientifically proven, trusted, and reliable, in supposed contrast to 'alternative' treatments. Yet, when Dr Omar Ahmed of Monash Medical Centre looked for the evidence in 2001, he found the following: there were no systematic reviews or meta-analyses of ETS; no evidence-based clinical practice guidelines; no comparative studies; and most startlingly of all, no randomised controlled trials. Another study, in Toronto, concluded that the operation "may be associated with many and potentially serious complications." and recommended randomised controlled trials to assess the efficacy and risks of the operation. Mr Mitra in London reported that he was doing up to five operations a day at £4,000 a throw. Multiplied around the world, this does suggest a certain vested interest in not conducting a randomised trial, lest the results are not unambiguously positive. It does strike me as odd that thousands of people are being led into an expensive operation that does not seem to have an objective measure of its efficacy or risks, when probably the majority of these operations are unnecessary because the blushing can be stopped with interactive hypnotherapy. Such is medicalisation!

Grown-ups often have no idea that the words they say in pure jest or with benevolent intentions may be given entirely literal and serious interpretations by a child, perhaps with very grave meanings than can crush some aspect of the child's spirit. The child, after growing up, may forget those words and yet retain the impact, the damage of "heavy words so lightly thrown" (as The Smiths put it in their song). Again, hypnotherapy lets you uncover the significance that was attached to those words.

Hypnosis is a voluntary state. A hypnotherapist cannot make you go into hypnosis. Rather, a hypnotherapist can help you into a state of hypnosis, as she can help you access your inner wisdom. Interactive hypnotherapy allows you to design your own labels and to edit out those that may have been given to you in the past. The great thing is that you get to be the designer. A skilled interactive hypnotherapist will know which questions to ask, and which suggestions to make, to help you get there.

Case study: Rebecca

Rebecca, aged 31, produces television documentaries and lives in London with her husband. She chose interactive hypnotherapy as a fast-track route to free herself from a lot of anger and resentment. Rebecca declared with a sense of genuine gratefulness "I have a fantastic life. I have achieved, and done, many amazing things". She continues, "but I felt lost, dissatisfied, and angry. I felt I was constantly proving myself. I felt resentful and that I'd had enough. I wasn't doing any of the things I wanted to do. It had got to the point where I was frustrated by everything, and was constantly fighting battles with myself. I love children. I love gardening. I wanted to define myself in other ways than by my job."

Rebecca was experiencing increasing levels of stress, and a sincere desire for change — to set new goals and address balance in her life. Rebecca viewed interactive hypnotherapy as a way forward to free herself from the negative feelings of 'anger', 'resentment', and 'dissatisfaction', which she realised were casting a shadow over an otherwise sunny life.

Rebecca enjoyed a wonderfully playful fun relationship with her husband and part of the 'resentment' and 'anger' was having her 'play time' with him squeezed. She sensed that a part of her was allowing work to encroach by not allowing and giving permission to herself to step back and recover control — to choose to be out, and away from work. A secure, confident, and unconditionally loving man, he had supported Rebecca in her choices.

Self-aware and responsible, she was very aware of not 'dumping' or ' projecting' her anger onto others — friends or family. These people offered her a haven and retreat — to be the loving and light and 'fun' person her nature sought to express. The drive and ambition that had fuelled a successful and distinguished career no longer tasted as inviting to the palate as once it had. Rebecca did not understand why she felt so angry when her life was so fantastic and she had realised her dreams and her dream job.

Rebecca did not over-eat, drink, or smoke, *she went shopping* — another favoured way of dealing with anger.

"I felt critical of everything, and really cross on the surface. Other colleagues made the leap and asked to work three days a week. I judged them as not being committed and felt angry. I was even more angry that they didn't lose their job title, their status, or their salary tag. Deep inside I wanted to do the same. It felt like I was imprisoned by my seven-days-a-week mentality, and my commitment to constantly work hard. I just wanted to break free. If they could do it, why couldn't I? My thoughts became increasingly negative and judgmental of myself and others, and seemed to take me down into emotional free-fall."

"Things that I'd usually taken in my stride as part of city life really irritated me — cancelled and late trains, supermarket queues, and packed, noisy restaurants where you couldn't hear yourself speak. If someone was unhelpful, thoughtless or rude I felt like screaming."

Cheryl Richardson, in her inspiring book, *Take Time For Your Life*, writes 'There is a growing need for more than what therapy provides. In therapy, clients talk about the changes they'd like to make in their lives, but the "how to" and the resources are often missing. Yet such information is often crucial to my clients' success. Clients want someone to help them design a new life. They want a guide who can anticipate the obstacles along the path to this new life and help them navigate around them. They want a partner who will remind them of their greatness when they forget, give them the tools to get unstuck, and challenge them to take action in spite of their fears. This need is now being met by personal coaches.'

When you arrive at Chapter 12 you will fully appreciate my being up and running with what Cheryl Richardson writes here. I acknowledge that a life coach is a great plus, as a personal fitness trainer is. I would like to champion life coaching one giant step further. For within *you* is a personal coach, and *you* can be your own best coach. Interactive hypnotherapy is a tool to facilitate your gaining access to and to switching that inner Personal Coach full on. Read on for how the inner coach surfaced and surprised Rebecca.

Rebecca felt a great pride in 'winning gold stars at school' and in hypnosis she was able to gain clarity and understanding that this was what continued to fuel her drive at work even though she already had 'won' enough gold stars to form a chain to light up the length and breadth of the *Thames*. In hypnotherapy she was able to acknowledge the truth. Rebecca did have sufficient stars to justify her position and job title and could stop "constantly proving herself".

Interactive hypnotherapy enabled Rebecca effectively to up-date her emotional CV and free herself from a negative, energy-eating emotion. She reported, "In hypnosis my anger came forward in the shape of a hard, fibrous triangle. My subconscious dissolved it, so much so, that I saw lots of little bubbles floating around. I felt I could breathe again. At the end of the first session I felt I could see the wood for the trees. By the time I arrived for the second session I felt I could allow for more balance in my life, and by the third, I felt sanguine and optimistic."

"I was constantly fighting battles with myself, torn between what I wanted to do and what I felt I should be doing. My work defined who I am. I had been mentally committed seven days a week. I thrived on the praise, and the success. I wanted to have time to paint, to garden and to make space in my life for children. Problem was I held a belief that I could not be successful unless I was mentally committed seven days a week. I was frightened of losing my job title, my status and my salary tag. My thinking really was my own worst enemy."

"By the third session, I had understood the life sentence that was imprisoning me. It ran along the lines of 'keep up the good work' day after day. And I was scared at what other people would think if I 'stopped keeping up the good work'. I also believed in spite of my success 'I was not good enough to stop.' Knowing the fuel that was driving me helped me change some things at work. Feeling guilty and feeling very responsible had blocked my ability to delegate. I formed a creative team. Helped by changing my belief system in such a way that I trusted others more to be as professional, trusting and caring as me, I created more time. By doing this I felt more empowered. Having taken action, I felt lighter and calmer. My anger had lifted. I had more time. Everything felt more possible again."

Rebecca is still in the same job with a fresh and more balanced perspective, mentally working three days a week instead of seven. "I feel happier than I have for a long time. I have a new and lovely office. All the things I do at work seem now to be very productive for me. I feel shiny-bright and I have trust and strength by my side. I have more time at weekends now for friends socialising, enjoying restaurants, bars, walking and picnics in the park."

"I admit I still define myself by what I do, but I now allow myself to define work as fun. I allow myself to delegate without feeling guilt and I pull back and read a book, or do something else".

11

◎

THE WONDERFUL WIZARD OF US!
Hypnotherapy shows you what you already have within yourself

When I put down the telephone, having spoken to potential clients, often-times I am drawn to consider the three characters in the film the *Wizard of Oz*, and in particular the three companions to Dorothy: the Scarecrow, the Tin Man and the Lion. What follows is a case study that illustrates that, just as those characters found what they were seeking inside themselves, so hypnotherapy can often reveal what you already possess. Each of those three characters is asking for a quality — an aptitude, or gift, call it what you may. You will surely recall, that the Scarecrow wishes to have a brain, the Tin Man wishes to have a heart and hence to have an emotional life, and the Lion, longs for courage and to be brave. In the course of the film, evidence mounts to the conclusion, that each of the three holds within themselves, the very qualities and aptitudes that they were off to see the wizard for. I do wonder whether, when the three arrive back at the Emerald city, the belligerence, and blustering frustration of The Wizard is in great part triggered by his incomprehension. Incomprehension that the three companions still do not get it! They do not yet grasp the truth of the matter — that within them already reside, the very qualities they continue to seek, — and which they believe only the supposed magical powers of the wizard can bestow upon them.

'Dorothy', a bright and generous professional, with many fans in the law firm in which she worked, telephoned to say her request for interactive hypnotherapy related to work. Where there might have been celebration in her voice, there was worry and fear. "I am being proposed for partnership. I have to say what it is that will make me an asset as a partner. At the moment, I can only focus on what it is that won't make me an asset as a partner. I think I need to change my mind around."

The truth of the matter began to unfold during our initial face-to-face conversation. As I had suspected, we were not alone. The Scarecrow, the Tin Woman and the Lion were an influencing presence. "I find it really, really painful to write about myself, and say how good I am," said Dorothy (unwittingly enacting the Tin Man).

"I have huge self-doubt," said Dorothy (as the Lion). " I think this is when they finally see through me and realise I'm a fraud."

"They'll realise I don't have a clue about anything" quickly chipped in Dorothy (now as Scarecrow).

"I've always hidden the fact that she is clever," confided Dorothy the Tin Man, to the shock and chagrin of Dorothy the Scarecrow. This was to protect younger Dorothy from being hurt by other boys and girls in her class at school.

Happily, unlike our three friends from the film, this real-life Dorothy did immediately get it! The three interactive hypno-therapy sessions became a celebration of Dorothy's gifts and talents. She was able to confirm that the competencies and attributes required for her to really go for this opportunity *were* very much embedded within her — that the very competencies and attributes she had perceived herself as lacking were simply in need of acknowledgement and a polish and shine — having sat under a bushel for so long, they were now ready to sing. So many gifted 'inner players' came out to play full out for Dorothy, and to reclaim her truth.

In hypnosis, together with her inner team, she practised declaring her truth, and practised declaring it in preparation for the presentations and the interviews that were to come in the days and weeks ahead. She practised declaring her cleverness, and re-hearsing her cleverness, coached by a growing sense of emotional safety in standing tall, standing brave, and standing successful. Dorothy allowed herself to shine. Some weeks after the last time we met, Dorothy rang to say that the partnership honour had been confirmed. Like the Lion, she had found the courage and the bravery to claim her kingdom, and to wear the crown.

There are many Tin Man, Scarecrow, and Lion characters amongst us, and many Dorothy characters too. Many of us experience a certain sense of lack of an emotional something. However, the words, the phrases, and the sentences that each one of us uses to explain our experience of 'lack' will be different in each and every case. Moreover, the words, the phrases, and the sentences that each one of us uses to describe how we want to experience the desired quality or behaviour will be different too. Invariably, people have virtues and qualities to different depths and degrees, and often in some, and less so in other different areas of our lives. Sometimes a person's wish for a quality, a virtue or a behaviour may be specific to a situation or an environment, or in relationship with a particular person.

Your language, your choice of vocabulary, and your special way of explaining, makes your session unique and tailored individually for you — the cut and the fit being shaped by how you choose to express yourself. As you will discover, language can be a revelation. Some of us are pre-disposed to use 'organ language' for example. We adopt expressions like 'knuckle under', 'breaking my heart', and the 'proverbial pain in the butt'. Often these expressions hold portent to a 'feeling' resonating at a deeper subconscious level. The conscious mind provides us with something like a print-out of what is going on 'downstairs' but, until we wake-up and recognise it, the print-out gets lost — as the next thought follows hot on the heels of the last. Potent revelations can easily get missed. Frankie's reflections illustrate this point.

Case Study: Frankie

Frankie chose interactive hypnotherapy to help her stop picking her fingers. On the initial session, she had admitted "I chew and I pick [my fingers] all day long. I'm embarrassed when I'm holding a cup of coffee. It stops me doing so many things. It is like a little hideaway. When instinct takes over, I *pick* it up straight away." On that first session, Frankie's subconscious had taken her on a journey of discovering the roots of the picking behaviour. Further insight had revealed why, when instinct took over, Frankie pick-[ed] it up straight away. As we spoke, on what was anticipated to be the final and the third session, she said, "I'm totally on my way. As the scenarios [when previously she picked] melt away, I become more focussed. *I have found myself with so much more time on my hands.*" Frankie skipped forward saying, "I used to do embroidery, dress-making, and design. I would like to get back to it." At this point I gently prompted her to reflect upon the words she had spoken: "I have found myself with so much more time on my hands." How prophetic and revealing our words can be revealed to be, when we begin to listen to ourselves.

Listening to ourselves can reveal a brighter side. And, astonishing though it may seem, there is always a brighter side. There may also be indications of the support to come, perhaps embedded within your apparent sense of lack, and your 'self-sentencing'. A very general illustration of this is the word 'imagine'. Clients often say, " I've always been like that, and I cannot *imagine* being any other way." " I think of myself as a smoker. I cannot imagine myself as not." The thing is, that what we tend to imagine day after day, week after week, tends to happen in reality. We have effectively programmed ourselves for the inevitable. Hypnotherapy is a way to begin to 'imagine' something rather different.

It is often the way that the words and phrases spoken in the presenting problem, cast important light on the seeds of potential strengths, lying dormant and waiting to grow.

Whatever you choose to tell your therapist, it is often the first sentence or the last — or indeed an afterthought, said just as you are about to begin — that provides the most revealing words or 'keys' to open the subconscious at the start of a session.

12

◎

ARE YOU SITTING COMFORTABLY?
Case studies in hypnotherapy

The therapeutic process begins, not when you step through the door, but when you make the appointment to come. This is why, if someone is making an enquiry about hypnotherapy on someone else's behalf, the therapist will always ask that the person make his own appointment. Making your own appointment is a declaration that you are choosing to come to hypnotherapy. By making this declaration, you activate your subconscious mind to commence the changes. So even before you settle down onto the hypnotherapist's chair you are beginning to change your mind. This underlines the fact that you are the one who is making all the changes. It is tempting, but completely mistaken, to imagine the hypnotherapist as a magician who will wave a magic pendulum and transform you. You are already the magician yourself, and the hypnotherapist's job is merely to guide you to the beneficial use of your own power to change your mind. Likewise, the process does not cease when you step out of the hypnotherapist's door. Your subconscious mind will continue to give you more — more insight, more connections. Your subconscious gradually increases the power of your inner light from a dim 25-watt bulb to 100 watts. These changes continue for your positive benefit.

Having made an appointment, clients often ask whether any preparation is necessary, and what to bring. No preparation is necessary, other than giving consideration to what you wish to achieve with the help of hypnotherapy — consideration that, in fact, most of you have already done before making the telephone call. And as to what to bring — well I suggest that you bring an open mind.

For those readers who are considering interactive hypno-therapy: please do bear in mind that what follows is *one* way, and that individual interactive hypnotherapists expand and develop their courses of training and study — such that they make what they learn into their own familiar procedure. The adage that there's nothing new under the sun is particularly pertinent at this point. At least, *there is very little new under the sun*. What I have aimed to do is to create a repertoire that may be made available to the many practising therapists for them to make their own.

Whole-Being Hypnotherapy, as my practice is called, has evolved over eight years of professional work. Whole-Being respects and embraces the wisdom within, and our individual ability to come forward with our own suggestions for change — suggestions that can enable and ennoble our lives. The creation of an 'inner team', and the notion of 'building an inner team' — to facilitate continuing inner 'life coaching' outside the session —

have themselves evolved, and grown from a grounding of firm foundations.

These foundations reside in the forward-thinking and modernising innovations of Valerie Austin, who recognised the potency of a selection of therapeutic techniques — which had previously been devised by past masters of hypnosis and therapy. These elements of technique formed a repertoire, or toolbox, that she worked with, and which she developed for a number of years with hundreds of clients. The sequence of events in her sessions was found to work elegantly and economically to elicit clean, fast, and effective change in those individuals who had chosen hypnotherapy, and particularly interactive hypnotherapy.

Like Valerie, I have found that, in the majority of client cases, interactive hypnotherapy effects its changes successfully and permanently within just one to five sessions, the average treatment taking three sessions.

Yes, some sessions do require more negotiation, more persuasion, and more choreography than others. Fresh steps do evolve with practice. Your own chosen therapist — by listening to, and trusting, her intuition — may introduce other steps and design your dance of life in a different way. Celebrate the difference! Different steps do take you to where you want to be. The interactive, and therapeutic, dance between both client and therapist is always in motion.

I often say to my clients that, as a therapist, I am a facilitator — a cheerleader, a partner in their dance — a player on their team. I sense the triggers in them that I need to activate along the journey, and I co-create the choreography as the session progresses. But it is you, the client, that creates the music, and the song.   It is your wisdom that provides the content. It is your words that heal. It is the wisdom that is within yourself that affords you the clarity and the understanding. Remember always — you are the composer and you are the arranger of your life's song and dance. Interactive hypnotherapy positions you to be in a state of relaxation to take hold of your creative reins and to steer a fresh course.

As the client, when you arrive at your first session, you will be invited to share more about your interest in hypnotherapy and your reason for coming. You will be asked: What do you want to achieve? How would you like to feel?   How would you like to experience yourself? In the case of smoking, you may be asked: Why have you decided to stop smoking now?   Or: What has prompted your decision to stop now?   In cases of weight loss, what weight would you ideally like to be? How do you want to perceive yourself and to be perceived by others? Or, even, what do you want to be called?

Sometimes a shortened form or 'pet' name is the name you most prefer. The therapist will use your name on several occasions during the session, because she will refer to you by name when talking to your subconscious. So it is important that the name that your therapist uses is the one with which you are most comfortable, and is the name that, in your view, honours and acknowledges you.

You do get to tell your story. But sometimes, when you tell it, you simply do not see the wood for the trees!

Case Study: Derek

Derek came to interactive hypnotherapy to broaden his diet. This is what he said: "I'm a plain eater. I want to be able to go into a restaurant and have other foods — Mediterranean foods. When I go out I can only have steak or Dover sole. I find I have a real problem with food, and I don't for the life of me know why." Having reported his conundrum, his *very next statement* was, "My father was a regimental Sergeant Major. If you didn't eat it, it was served the next day."

But, and it is a big but, interactive hypnotherapy makes no assumptions. Wisdom does not jump to conclusions! In hypnosis, your subconscious can come up with something surprisingly and completely different to that you have talked about 'consciously'. A client can speak of a need for Confidence, and in hypnosis, Strength comes forward as a manifestation of it.

However, as it turned out, Derek had 'hit the nail on the head'! In hypnosis he met with his younger self, sitting at table before a plate full of "boiled potatoes, cabbage and some form of meat". Alongside him were his mum and his dad insisting, "You *have* to eat it! You'll get nothing else!"

Derek held a lengthy and private conversation with his parents and his younger self inside the hypnosis session, and came out of the discussions and negotiations determined — determined to seek out strange tastes, variations and combinations. The 'inner player' who was named Determined stuck by him. Derek returned for the follow-up session, ten days later, relishing more than just the relishes! He had entered a kingdom of garlic king prawns, and salad, and had eaten tomatoes too! "I'm just getting on with it!" he declared. His social life had improved, and he was learning to cook. Mediterranean style of course!

A hypnotherapist is stepping into your reality, and your story is fully accepted. Remember, though, that the stories are your own personal and subjective history. You can make history. You can create history. And you can re-write history. Your history may take two, five, ten, minutes, or fifteen. Bright, intelligent people can talk and talk, and talk. Many of us can talk for several chapters and the subconscious may not get a word in edgeways. Within twenty or so minutes your hypnotherapist is likely to have got the gist from what you say.

Your therapist, who has tuned her mind into your spoken wavelength, will listen intently, and may take notes with an obvious and apparent degree of keenness. The reason for this is to track your language. She is particularly interested in the choice of words you use. The focus is on *your* vocabulary — the words — the phraseology — the life-sentences that you use to describe your experience of yourself. Although your history may not have been fully told, nevertheless your hypnotherapist, by listening out loud, will have received the essential ingredients to begin your session. This is sufficient to start work, because the therapeutic process is propelled by your personal suggestions and images. This is why interactive hypnotherapy does not require the taking of a long case history, and does not require a theory-laden diagnosis. More often the diagnosis is a 'spiritual' diagnosis, one that emerges from your vocabulary. Words such as 'restless', 'impatient' and 'angry' may spiritually be diagnosed as a lack of peace; 'fear' and 'insecurity', a lack of love.

Your hypnotherapist will latch onto both the precise words you use, and will focus on key words and phrases when you talk about yourself. A word, a phrase, or a sentence, perhaps if it is frequently repeated, may stand out. Sometimes you may use a word or phrase in a different, interesting, and positively revealing way — a word that is used in a way that may be out of the usual context and so suggests 'keys' that can be turned to open hidden doorways to growth.

Case Study: Apala

Speaking of depression, Apala reported, "...there have been 'no achievements' in the way I behave or the way that I think." Our previous session had revealed that Apala was 'in the habit' of running her relationship with Satish as though he was part of a bid to achieve a grade 'A' examination pass. Meeting her Asian parent's academic dreams had driven Apala to study consistently — and exclusively of anything much else in her early years. Success was secured under pressure, and in the face of underlying fear. Apala had achieved the grades. Now the habit had taken a

less appropriate, clinging hold — played out in her communications with Satish.   Apala acknowledged that this clingy
behaviour was detrimental to an otherwise happy and loving
relationship. "He says that he feels under pressure all the time to
do things that will make me happy irrespective of his own needs."
In a state of relaxation, Apala went back to her teenage years, and
her younger self provided massive clarity and understanding.
"I'm studying. I'm about fifteen — at high school. I'm in a state
of panic. I can't do the maths homework. They [my parents] try to
help, but they can't understand why I can't do it. If I can't do the
work, and can't pass the exam no one will want me. No one will
marry me. I'll be alone."

Sometimes what we 'carry' is emotional weight. In general,
once a person lets go of the emotional weight, physical weight can
also begin to disappear. Remember that, within the subconscious,
symbolic or figurative ideas have the same weight as literal ones.
The subconscious does not share the conscious mind's concern
with literal truth.

Case Study: Monica

Talking about her weight, Monica said, "I 'carry weight', but I do
not look as heavy as I am."   In a state of hypnosis, Monica's young
self revealed, "I'm alone in the living room of the house where we
live. I'm watching out for the postman. I'm waiting for a letter.
Every year I have been going to summer camp and the letter will
tell me I have got a place." The young girl had watched out for
several days, but this year the letter never came. An explanation

eventually emerged. Money within the family was tight, and her parents could no longer afford to pay for her to participate. Speaking consciously, Monica shared that she had never wanted to come home from the summer camp. Her mother was an alcoholic and the summer camp was a very consistent place to be.

Your hypnotherapist will use a word or a phrase precisely. She will use your words verbatim. They are *your* words, *your* phrases, and *your* self-sentencing sentences that form the key to the success of an interactive hypnotherapy session. Sentences are different, and vary in length. They vary from a few years to tens of years. Sentences do not give you time off for good behaviour. Sentences run concurrently and continuously. Sentences are often — for life. Then one day there is a dawning. Then one day you want out. You now want to spin a different line.

Perhaps you apply for a job — one that you are already amply qualified and experienced to do. Nevertheless, maybe because of a rogue belief, or a notion of lack — often a lack of confidence — you fluff the interview, fumble your way through the five-minute presentation. And you're mad with yourself, disappointed, and now driven to change. The going often has to get so bad, and uncomfortable for us to acknowledge the drivers within ourselves, ones that know we can change, and know we can be different. Finally you say; "Now I think I'm getting thwarted. Up until now I've coped with it. I'm just fed up with it. Now I want to address it."

"Since childhood, if I got a good exam result I've thought ... They must have got it wrong! I was just lucky. Just don't say anything. Automatically I say 'You can't do that' — *automatically*. I think I must have a certain level of confidence. It's more like a sense of social discomfort. I can appear sullen and quiet, and unassertive when I'm meeting and greeting people." Finally you ask, "Why?" and "I want to know the reason for this".

Permission to use certain words, phrases, and some sentences, will generally be sought, particularly when highly sensitive, or potentially traumatic. Clients who seek help to free themselves from a phobia, may, in an initial session, not feel comfortable with the specific name of their fear being spoken. A woman who sought help for a phobia of moths could not bear even to hear the word "moth" spoken.

Whatever you choose to tell your therapist, it is often the first sentence or the last — or indeed an afterthought, said just as you are about to begin, that provides the most revealing words or keys to open the subconscious at the start of a session. Glance over the beginning sentences that follow.

Some beginning sentences:

"I'm a bit shy."

"I suffer from a strong inferiority complex that affects my communication..."

"I'm feeling really uptight..."

"I do not have too much faith in myself..."

"I know what I want to say, but it comes out mumbled."

"I'm always unhappy. There's always something new I find that's wrong."

"I feel restricted in a life sense. Little things are becoming really big."

Some ending sentences:

"I cry in my sleep and I don't know why?"

"Sometimes I go out of my way not be with people."

"At the moment I do not think I can handle things."

"Why does sleep upset me so irrationally?"

"I don't feel clever."

Many potentially positive, persuasive words stand out, dressed in a less-than-empowering cloak of context. 'Strong', 'Faith' and 'feel Clever' stand out, together with the phrase 'I know what I want to say' — providing plenty of scope for movement and progression towards confidence, self-esteem, self-belief, clarity, relaxation and so on. Your vocabulary, in a variety of contexts, begins to prepare your case, but your case most certainly does not rest there. There may be several sentence options. The session commences with the sentence that resonates with you the most. Occasionally, there may be two or more words, phrases or sentences that hold portent to the 'problem'.

Here is Hannah's opening story. "I am in a constant state of fear of other people. I do things because of other people. Most of my motivations are external. I'd like to find the motivation from within myself. To be more focussed. To lose some weight. To get back to being the size I was.

Health and human nutrition is fundamental to me. I want to find the strength from within, and to take responsibility."

You may be asked which of those words, phrases, and sentences (all of which describe the same experience in slightly different ways) best suggest for you the starting point for the initial enquiry? In essence, what do you regard as the priority — taking what you have just shared as the starting point? This is not an over-simplification of the problem, but a way of getting a handle on it that we can then use to open the session. Let us first distinguish those initial three sentences in the example just given.

1. I am in a constant state of fear of other people.
2. I do things because of other people.
3. Most of my motivations are external.

Secondary to the three beginning sentences are the issues of 'lack': lack of focus; and lack of strength — and the perceived inability to take responsibility for her life. Remember that inter-active hypnotherapy is concerned not only with 'what's wrong with you.' It looks beyond the veil of your vocabulary to locate and invoke 'what is right with(in) you.' Hannah included the words: Focus, Strength, and Responsibility. These words hold presentiments of what is to come. These words suggest some of the seeds that are awaiting verbal nutrition and encouragement to grow. These words suggest a team — an inner team that is awaiting its training — in the wings, on the stage of her life.

Weight issues are included in Hannah's ring of changes too, although the word "weight" did not enter into her initial sentences. Perhaps it is worth repeating that when people let go of any emotional weight(s) that they are carrying around it is generally the case that their physical weight can begin to go down too.

You get to choose which of the words or phrases reflects your most pressing experience of yourself. These kinds of opportunities to participate illustrate the driving force you play in a session. It is important that the question posed is made up of words that resonate especially well for you at the present time — that they form a question that can best generate the way forward for change for you.

In interactive hypnotherapy, this is how those three possible sentences would be presented back to the subconscious.

1. Hannah reports to me she is in a constant state of fear of other people. What is the reason for this?

2. Hannah reports to me she does things because of other people. What is the reason for this?

3. Hannah reports to me most of her motivations are external. What is the reason for this?

The pivotal starting point will therefore normally be the sentence you choose to open the session, or maybe the concluding sentence of your opening. Whatever that is, the therapist will model her first sentence on it. Rest assured that whichever sentence you do choose does not exclude the others. They are all part and parcel of the same presenting problem. Any one of them would lead you progressively towards the positive outcome you want to achieve. The choice is yours. Go with your gut feeling — your intuition, and you will 'sense' the sentence that is nearest to the underlying reason for whatever the problem is.

What is the reason? Consciously of course you do not know the reason. That is why you have come to interactive hypnotherapy. Of course you may have ideas and cogent opinions, and you may be holding a heavily weighted and onerous theory of your own problem. You may have otherwise discovered that you can talk weekly for fifty-five minutes and fifty-five seconds in analysis sessions about the problem. Furthermore, you may talk forever and a day to yourself internally. Your inner judge and jury do not need much sleep. However, you may have yet to discover what your inner wisdom thinks about the problem, and how that deeper wisdom can potentially help you feel different and feel free.

So — with the opening sentence chosen, and with you finding yourself in a much, much, more relaxed state, the interactive dialogue can begin. Interactive hypnotherapy does not require an initial consultation, with a view to starting on the second visit. No! Interactive hypnotherapy commences on the first visit. The average attendance is three sessions, but it can be just two sessions, or even just one. The stopping smoking therapy is invariably one session, with the option of a back-up session included within a six-month period.

Your vocabulary has prepared your case, and that is by far the best way to have worked out 'the therapy specifically for you', and 'the therapy personal to you'.

Within the hypnotic session, it is a common practice to bring forth visualisations or to 'sense' people who have played a part in your personal history. A dialogue will then ensue between you and these recalled individuals. The recalled individuals may include yourself as a younger person, perhaps a child or a teenager, and family members, teachers, and friends. To be respectful of your integrity, many of these dialogues can be said privately within. The therapist does not need to hear them. That is entirely up to you, and how you feel. Aloud or privately said, the words are of equal force. That goes for suggestions and ideas from within too. These conversations can last seconds or minutes, and sometimes some of those recalled people who are gathered together on your inner stage may dry up — not know what to say, or have nothing to say. Remember, your therapist will handle anything you say, and she will handle nothingnesses. If nothing comes forward in response to a question, you will find that there is always another way. Your therapist will guide you though the pauses, the lulls, and the times when your subconscious, or the recalled individuals, say nothing, or refuse to speak. When a conversation comes to a standstill or ends, then saying 'Yes' or making a small gesture with as little as a finger will suffice to indicate that you are ready to continue the process.

Case Study: Jill

Sometimes you can expect the unexpected.

Jill's widowed mother is on her own. It is late, and she is working in the house. To Jill her mother is everything. The child worries for her mother's health, aware of the hours she works every day. Now, having returned from her paid work, the mother is absorbed in cleaning the home — oblivious to her small daughter's worry, and feelings of 'Scared' — lying in bed, in her room. This account alludes to a case of anxiety. Worry had fermented into a general pattern of anxiety over a period of two decades, building to an unpleasant crescendo — one that, today, we label 'panic attack.' " In October my mother told me she had cancer. Now, it's like there's a ball of nerves wound up all the time." In hypnosis Jill's subconscious was asked the reason for the ball of nerves. The answer came forward as 'Scared'. Within the hypnosis session, by invitation from her young daughter, the mother put down her mop and bucket and came to be with her child — to sit by her bedside and to listen. Her young daughter was able literally and metaphorically to get the feelings of 'Scared' off her chest.

She said to her mother, "I'm worried. I want you to look after yourself and to be careful. I do not want you to be alone, and I don't want to be left alone without you."

The mother listened. The child needed to be heard, and to have her feelings of concern validated. The session did not touch specifically on her mother's current health condition — one that had this far been successfully treated. The session dealt with the feelings of being Scared 'in childhood' — held for so long as a 'ball of nerves'. The ball of nerves dissolved.

With the strong support of Reassurance on Jill's team, Jill sensed she was free of worry. On the follow-up session she reported, "I realised the big ball in my stomach had completely gone, and it hasn't come back."

The healing in hypnosis rests upon the simple fact that, within the state of hypnosis, your subconscious has great difficulty in telling the difference between doing something in reality, and doing it in hypnosis. That 'something' can be words you wish to say or words you wish to hear someone else say. They can be words you need to say in response to another's off-the-cuff comment, or cutting comment, or comment said in a fit of pique — a long time, or an eternity ago. They can be words of preparation and rehearsal — for a job interview; a job appraisal; a presentation; a public speaking engagement; a wedding speech; or an audition for an artistic performance.

Case Study: Eleanor

Eleanor initially came for hypnotherapy to help her to "wake up and face the day".

She returned one week later, smiling broadly, saying, "I have taken a step forward. My spirit is different. I feel better and stronger. I wake up ready to do something". But she was now facing a dilemma. A counsellor, whom she had been on a waiting list to see for some weeks, had now become available. She felt duty bound to honour the referral, especially as her GP had pre-scribed the counselling. In the space of the past seven days, however, she had found that her past experience, which had so dominated her every day, had now lost its power of repression and depression. She had regained control of something that had been emotionally overwhelming her for more than a year. She had moved forward into a new space, where she was focussing on new possibilities as opposed to old *im*possibilities. Now, after twenty years of successful employment, any further conversation about the 'betrayal' in her past, which had been the original source of her problem, held little interest for her. Talking about the problem would mean re-entangling with the depression she was now moving beyond. Consciously, Eleanor said, "I want to be stronger and to be successful. I want to be heard. I do not want to be over-looked. I want to be respected."

During the second session under hypnosis she was ment-ally surrounded by a championing, supportive 'inner team' of characters who were aspects of her personality — called Con-fidence, Strength, Belief, and Faith — which she had nominated and called forth to be with her. She proclaimed of herself, "To-gether with Belief and Faith she *can* do it. Between the four of them, she is *going* to do it. She has to be able to concentrate, and it will come. She will enjoy the new job so very much! She will be *acknowledged in her work,* and be *respected*. She knows what it is like to be at the bottom. She will help others come out on top. She will have a fine position. She will concentrate and she will see that she is liked. As her role in this new job grows, so will she."

And at the end of the second session of hypnosis, Eleanor spoke about the future that she was celebrating. She said of her new self: "She's so happy. She's up with the lark. She's dealing with people. She keeps laughing. It's not long before her managers realise what a gem she is. They want her to do well, and they want her to stay. She's good at her job, and enjoys the people around her. She will be respected and she will be loved. I'm so excited for her."

Interactive hypnotherapy does not actually involve re-experiencing the full emotional backdraft of an event, a situation, or a circumstance in your life. The skill of the hypnotherapist is to help you be your own 'private detective' by guiding you back to the event, for the purpose of identification. Emotions may well be released in the course of the identification. There may be tears of compassion for the younger self, of acknowledgement of the grief, the loss, and also the profound relief — "the joy of our sorrow unmasked", as Kahlil Gibran wrote. Welcome the tears. The session makes space for tears, as it makes space for laughter and smiles. You move through the actual emotions that belong to that time, and you move on to a chosen place of safety, security and perhaps beauty, before any appropriate further discussions and enlightenment can take place. You do not stay in the past. You do not rest in the past hurt or trauma. You touch the past and move into the future, which is full of light. These discussions and negotiations have the effect of neutralising the emotion and in helping to transmute the destructive memory into a potent force for reconstruction. With a sense of clarity and understanding can come a metaphorical and actual deep healing from within. The 'event' or the 'situation' takes on a different perspective, having gained access to the truth. It is not belittled, devalued, erased or forgotten about. Rather, it is re-contextualised. It is no longer king. You give the memory a new context, in which it no longer drags you down and anchors you to the past..

Case Study: Lucia

Some years ago, a Brazilian woman called Lucia came to my practice. Lucia lectured in Sociology at the university in São Paulo, and was on an extended vacation studying English in London. The sabbatical was a gift to herself having come through a cancer. She was fifty years of age, and had been told her cancer was in recession. To maintain this bill of clear health, Lucia had committed herself to a macrobiotic diet. In spite of this, her energy levels and her health could dip severely, so much so that occasionally her body would convey upon her a day of rest. Her body's insistence on rest and retirement during her most precious of days in London had elicited an emotional disruption and an anger, that she was being denied full participation in her programme of study and sight-seeing in a city that she had since childhood longed to visit. She lamented, "I cannot live like this. I do all the right things. I follow a disciplined diet and I get sufficient periods of rest. Why am I so lacking in sufficient energy to get me through these days?"

In hypnosis Lucia skipped all of the preliminaries, and observed herself as a small child in darkness. And the first utterance of the small child was this. "I can't live like this." Gently I asked, "Where are you, little one?", and she answered, "I'm in a garage. There are no windows. My Father and Mother are there. I know that my Father cannot afford anywhere else for us to live. Now, he needs to sell the piano. I cannot live like this." "How old are you", I asked. "I am five."

I wondered then and there whether the seeds of Lucia's cancer had planted in the mind of her younger self who knew there was another life.

Within the hypnosis session, young Lucia was taken by her mother to a São Paulo park close by. She talked about her love of the flowers and of the light. Her older, grown-up self came to join her and to tell her how her life changed over the years. She came to set her free, from a sentence that had defined her life. She told her how Lucia had realised her dream, of an education, of a comfortable home, her professional life, and of her friends and colleagues, and especially of her trip to London. Grown-up Lucia was able to let the little girl know that she did not continue to live as then, and to bring the small child into the material and spiritual comfort of the here and now — to show her how she really lived now. The pain, the grief, and the bereavement compacted together in the form of a wooden coffin — Lucia's symbolic interpretation of her new perspective on dead and buried feelings. An angel stepped forward with a beautiful commemorative grave-stone. The burial, the reunion, and the celebration of the change, culminated in Lucia's proclaiming in hypnosis. "I am alive! I am alive!" Lucia moved from a position of pain, grief, and bereavement to a position of pageantry — a pageant that young Lucia had the energy and the health to lead, hand in hand with her grown-up self. And it was one that, in hypnosis, she rehearsed and that she would continue to lead energetically and healthily year after year, and well into her future. If not magic, this one-off session was a magical miracle.

The interactive dialogues are spoken in respectful and encouragingly hushed and deferential tones — often in whispers. The *timing* and the *rhythm* of the dialogue are *essential* to the choreography of the dance. It may be helpful to imagine the exchange as a dialogue in a broadcast radio play. In real time, you can ask your therapist to speed up, when you seem to be ahead of the game, or slow down, and to repeat words, phrases and questions if you drift off. There is a sense of drama created by tone of voice and nuance. In a similar way the voice of your therapist sets the stage. The therapist's presence helps to invoke the lighting, and their stage directions are the setting to facilitate your performance to shine. Moreover, this dramatic licence is employed to engender feelings of safety, of reassurance, of protection, of love, of awe, and of reverence. The voice is an exquisite instrument. The voice of your therapist can be one of presence and of promise. It can be a voice that evokes trust and healing. It can be loving, sensitive, understanding, reassuring, attentive, supportive, and strong. A voice can hold you steady through moments of release, encouraging you to welcome your tears. When you let the emotion out, there is then room for something else. Space for a voice that sweeps you ever higher in moments of happy realisation, clarity, jubilation and excitement. There is often a 'body sense' too – a sense of feeling lighter, or freer, and even cleaner, in the body as well as in the mind.

The 'stage directions' are spoken to engender a realm of wonder. You do enter a realm of wonder during an interactive hypnotherapy session, for there is a sense of awe created by discovering the clarity and wisdom within — as well as the love within. As I wrote previously in *Mind Detox*:

> "As human beings, we seek to understand why something has happened, why someone said something with particular words, or particular intonation, which lashed us so deeply. To understand, that is all. Quite often, with understanding follows a clearer sense of vision, and a tremendous sense of healing, and of being healed."

The interactions build to a celebratory sense of crescendo as the constructive agencies of your mind work together as an inner team that champions you. When *you* have turned the key, your therapist's voice can throw wide open the gates you've push ajar. Welcome Freedom! Welcome Confidence! Welcome Liberation! The voice of your therapist is a chorus line to your song, as she repeats, and repeats, and repeats, the best and the brightest of your lyrics. The echo feeds back to your subconscious and validates it. The more often you are exposed to an idea, the more it seeps through and influences you. Your hypnotherapist repeats essentially and verbatim your words, and champions with vigour the positive and affirming declarations you have chosen for yourself. She thereby effectively turns up the volume on your channel for change, so loud that it vibrates through your whole being. She helps ring in the repetition on *your* expressed suggestions for change. Your vocabulary effectively leads the way.

Constructive team players and positive aspects of your mind are welcomed with a touch of the cavalier — they are announced in swashbuckling style! They are cheerleaders! These words are often the new designer labels that you have chosen. These are the labels by which you now declare yourself to *be*. So they now have the opportunity to blow their own trumpet on behalf of you. This goes against the grain of the self-deprecating conservatism and pandemic cynicism of British culture, where blowing your own trumpet is held to be bad form, and definitely not cricket, if not downright sinful. For all things, however, there is a season. And your hypnotherapy is where you are given permission to blow your trumpet. This is the time and place where you are called upon to trumpet your successes and achievements, your brightness and your potential. Your inner team is here and they have a job of work to do. Here they come!

Confidence *strides* forward.

Courage *steps* forward.

Energy *bounds* forward.

Calm *breezes* into mind.

Peace and Relaxation *flow* through your whole being.

Yes! Yes! Yes!

Although team players at first come forward at full pelt, willingly and enthusiastically, nevertheless they sometimes appear to falter when asked to walk their talk. Confidence declares "I'm not going to be blocked!" Then, when asked to share whatever bright ideas and suggestions come into mind, he explains, "It's difficult to know where to start. I haven't had much of a chance to shine." Encouraged further to share whatever pops into mind, be it one word or two, he may remain silent — seemingly well and truly lost for words. Help is always at hand, in the form of two specialist reserves — Creative and the reserve team player Wise. Both are excellent at generating ideas when another team member has become lost for words. Most team players are happy to be encouraged to consult with either of Creative or Wise, and sometimes ask to consult with both. You may trust that at least one of them will be positioned to offer counsel.

And, yes, we do all have Creative and Wise reserve players available to us. I acknowledge that some clients are astonished that creativity and wisdom could ever be manifested on their inner teams. Rest assured that both are potentially present. In *Mind Detox* I reflected,

"Perhaps you relegated Creativity to the junior league when a voice announced you were not very good at drawing or singing at ten years of age. Most of us just need to re-frame our perception of how we view creativity. Creativity enters into so many of our day-to-day decisions. You are creative when you 'creatively' perform tasks in your own special idiosyncratic way. That really is being creative!"

You may imagine Wise as a sage of some sort, or as a large dusty, leather-bound book from which you need to remember to brush the dust off from time to time, and to gain access to the wisdom that it holds. Those pages may provide the wisdom to illuminate the dusty paths leading in directions that you have long forgotten, and over which layers of stress, tension or stifling self-criticism have settled over the years.

Get ready! — In this case it was player Wise who helped coach team player Confidence into a higher league. These are the strategies Wise suggested:

◎   do not be intimidated by people;

◎   be more relaxed;

◎   think positively;

◎   push fear away;

◎   do not mind so much.

Confidence was asked whether he was ready and willing to embrace those wise suggestions. "Of course! Yes!" was the immediate response. Having embedded those strategies, deeply within the foundations of his inner mind, Confidence was then invited to take a look inside his being, and to sense his inner light beginning to shine. What did he find therein? "That it lights me up!" When asked how that felt, he smiled a sensational smile and said, "Feels good!"

Your inner team is encouraged and supported in all ways to champion you. Your team is dressed in your chosen true colours. This is a team that, day after day, is prepared to play full out for *your* success. This team, tuned and fine-tuned for *your* brightest and for *your* best — *your* positive power for good — will continue to coach you, and to feed you with a beneficial diet for the mind — especially for your inner mind. This inner team, chosen by you, gives you, and persists in giving you, the best life-coaching you can get, because it comes from *within you*. Inside you resides profound wisdom, and a knowing of what is right for your life.

Your inner team continues to coach you over the next seven to ten, to fourteen days. Words and ideas that have been planted will germinate, then they will put down roots, will spread out tendrils and branches. They will grow in size and strength and make contact with like-minded thoughts and inclinations. The inner team will tend and nurture this luxuriant emotional re-growth. So, I generally suggest a follow-up session of hypno-therapy, following the initial session within seven to ten days. At the follow-up session, your therapist will ask you what you have experienced during the intervening period. The answers can vary from a sense of some sort of change, to amazing difference, or to little or no difference at all. To the latter clients, I always make the suggestion that on the first session one is planting seeds, and on the second, watering them, and on the third strengthening the growth. If you have not noticed a difference after the first session, trust that the second is usually likely to make more impact.

On a follow-up session, the primary importance of your vocabulary still holds good, and sets the stage for what then happens in that session. What you say, and what you report are, as before, presented verbatim, and at length, and with enthusiasm, gratitude and warmth. Here is an opportunity to thank your sub-conscious, and another opportunity to sing your words and praises, to sing your chorus of success.

The difference in subsequent sessions is in the continuation sentence. Having reported the best and the brightest, you will be asked how would you like to continue. Often the obvious next step is consolidation, and inner strengthening. It may be that what you wanted to avoid has occurred, and is still hampering you in some specific situations and environments, or with a certain individual with whom you have to have a relationship, often at work. In these cases choosing your words and phrases to introduce these *specific* occurrences the hypnotherapist can direct the session to home in on these finer details. You may say something along the lines of 'I want to know in my mind, that whatever happens I can handle it.'

When change has not been experienced at all, your hypnotherapist may refer back to the opening sentence — the one that began your initial session. During the intervening days, your subconscious may have given you more food for thought, in the sense you have now become ready to refine the opening sentence to reflect the real truth of the matter. Do take this as change. For, clarity is an important breakthrough in its own right, and you know that change always flies close on clarity's tail.

Here is an example of how a second session may progress the therapy.

Case study continued

Apala reported to me that she is 'getting more confident at work. Now work is a challenge. She no longer gets overwhelmed. She is quite amazed! She has generally relaxed a lot more. Now she feels she can go back and be more positive about it. Her old manager knows that she is doing well. She is a lot stronger. And her boyfriend, too, he is a lot happier that she is a lot stronger. Apala now reports that she wants to know in her own mind that whatever happens in her life, she can handle it. What needs to be in place for Apala to know in her own mind that whatever happens, she can handle it? A word will come forward.

A more general, catch-all continuation sentence would be along the lines of, 'What needs to be in place for this positive and strong progress to continue?' Some word or other will thereupon come forward.

And when there is no lasting change, a continuation sentence may commence as follows: "Joe reports to me he has experienced no difference at all, and is still experiencing *[the problem]*, what is the reason for this?" Alternatively: "Joe reports to me that he felt better for the first few days, and then it came back. What is the reason for it coming back?" Some word or other will then come forward.

In reporting back to the subconscious that there has been little or no change, the tone continues to be solicitous, gently and encouragingly enquiring. The subconscious has not done anything wrong by not manifesting significant change in the initial session. It has not failed you. Clarity may in fact be the beginning of your breakthrough. In your individual case, your subconscious may need a little more time to trust the process and be open to the change. Your subconscious may be slowly cooking.

There is no shame, and there is no blame. Interactive hypnotherapy is a loving, considerate, and patient process.

Be open to what happens next, and excited about the next stage of the hypnotherapeutic journey.

Afterword

Courtesy of *The Sound of Music*
I Have Confidence

What will this day be like? I wonder.
What will the future be? I wonder.
It could be so exciting to be out in the world,
to be free
My heart should be wildly rejoicing
Oh, what's the matter with me?
I've always longed for adventure
To do the things I've never dared
And here I'm facing adventure
Then why am I so scared
A captain with seven children
What's so fearsome about that?
Oh, I must stop these doubts, all these worries
If I don't I just know I'll turn back
I must dream of the things I am seeking
I am seeking the courage I lack
The courage to serve them with reliance
Face my mistakes without defiance
Show them I'm worthy
And while I show them
I'll show me
So, let them bring on all their problems
I'll do better than my best
I have confidence they'll put me to the test
But I'll make them see I have confidence in me

Besides which you see I have confidence in
me!
Somehow I will impress them
I will be firm but kind
And all those children (Heaven bless them!)
They will look up to me
And mind with each step I am more certain
Everything will turn out fine
I have confidence the world can all be mine
They'll have to agree I have confidence in
me
I have confidence in sunshine
I have confidence in rain
I have confidence that spring will come
again
Besides which you see I have confidence in
me
Strength doesn't lie in numbers
Strength doesn't lie in wealth
Strength lies in nights of peaceful slumbers
When you wake up – Wake Up!
It tells me all I trust I lead my heart to
All I trust becomes my own
I have confidence in confidence alone
(Oh help!)
I have confidence in confidence alone

Bibliography

Books

Austin, Valerie 1994 *Self Hypnosis*, Thorsons/Element Books, London.

Bramwell, M. 1928 *Hypnotism*, J.R. Lippencott Co., New York.

Dann, Brian Poetic Licence Issue 12, Published by Poetic Licence. ISSN 1360-0974

Cameron, Julia, 1995 *The Artists Way*, 2nd edition, Pan Books, Macmillan Publishers Ltd, London Cooke, Charles Edward, and A.E. Van Vogt 1965 *Hypnotism Handbook*, 2nd edition, Borden Publishing Co., Alhambra, California.

Kirtley C, in association with W. Proudfoot, 1990 *Consumer Guide to Hypnosis*, Two Factor Companies, Scarborough.

Kuhn, L., and Salvatore Rosso 1947 *Modern Hypnosis*, Borden Publishing Co., Alhambra, California.

LeCron, Leslie M., and J. Bordeaux 1947 *Hypnotism Today*, Grune & Stratton, New York.

Lilly, John C. 1972, *The Center of the Cyclone*, Julian Press, Inc., New York, NY, USA.

Lovell, Mary S. 1998, *A Rage To Live*, Abacus, A division of Little, Brown and Company (UK).

Marshall-Warren, Deborah 1999, *Mind Detox*, Thorsons/Element Books, London.

McGill, Ormond 1981, *Hypnotism & Meditation*, Westwood Publishing Company, USA.

Milgram, Stanley 1983, *Obedience to Authority: An Experimental View*, Harper Collins, New York.

Mowbray, Richard 1995, *The Case Against Psychotherapy Registration* Trans Marginal Press, London.

Pace, Anthony 1996 Maltese Prehistoric Art 5000-2500 BC, Fondazzjoni Patrimonju Malti.

Richardson, Cheryl 1999, Take Time for Your Life, Broadway Books, New
York
Robertson, Ian 2002, *The Mind's Eye*, Bantam Books, London.
Sheehan, Elaine 1995, *Self Hypnosis*, Thorsons/Element Books, London
Spiegel, Herbert, and David Spiegel 1978 *Trance and Treatment: Clinical
Uses of Hypnosis*, Basic Books, Inc., New York.
Storr, Anthony 1989, *Solitude, A Return to the Self*, Ballantine Books, New
York.
Tart, Charles (editor) 1969, 2nd ed 1972, Altered States of Consciousness,
Doubleday Anchor, Garden City, NY.
Tebbetts, Charles 1987 *Self Hypnosis*, Westwood Publishing Company,
USA.
Melchior, Thierry 1999, *Freud and hypnosis: The hypno-suggestive roots of the
Oedipus complex*, The Milton H. Erickson Foundation Newsletter
Vol. 19, No 1, Spring 1999
Udolf, Roy 1981 *Handbook of Hypnosis for Professionals*, Van Nostrand
Reinhold Co., New York.
Valley, Jerry, 1990, *Inside Secrets of Stage Hypnosis*, Jerry Valley
Productions.

Articles

BBC News Online, *Court victory for hypnosis woman*, 25th May 2001.
Graves, David, *Stage hypnotist 'brought back drama of sex abuse'*, Daily
Telegraph Online, 22nd May 2001.
Matthews, Robert *How one in five have given up smoking*, New Scientist, 31
October 1992
Milgram, Stanley, *Behavioral Study of Obedience*, Journal of Abnormal
Social Psychology (volume 67, pp 371-378), 1963.
Nash, Michael R. *The Truth and the Hype of Hypnosis*, Scientific American,
July 2001
O'Keefe, Tracie, *The case of a woman who died after being a volunteer in a stage
hypnosis show*, research paper, www.tracieokeefe.com, 1998.

UK Government

The Hypnotism Act 1952, HMSO.

Stage Hypnotism: Review of the Hypnotism Act 1952. Home Office
    Circular No. 39/1996. (Supersedes the Annex to the Home Office
    Circular No. 42/1989.)

Films

Campion, Jane (director). *Holy Smoke*, FilmFour4/Miramax International,
    1999, based on the book of the same name by Jane Campion and
    Anna Campion (1999).
Fleming, Victor (director). *The Wizard of Oz*, Metro-Goldwyn-Mayer, 1939,
    based on the book by L. Frank Baum
Stevenson, Robert (director). *Mary Poppins*, Walt Disney, 1964, based on
    the book Mary Poppins by P.L. Travers
Wise, Robert (director) *The Sound of Music*, 20th Century Fox, 1965, based
    on Maria von Trapp's autobiography of 1949.
Howard, Ron (director) *A Beautiful Mind*, Dreamworks & Universal, 2001.
Friedlander, Louis (director) *The Raven*, Universal, 1935, based on Edgar
    Allen Poe's poem of 1915.

Paintings

The Whitechapel Art Gallery Centenary Review catalogue 2001
Hockney, David The Hypnotist, 1963, oil on canvas, 214 x 214 cm.

I'm **afraid** of **hypnosis**   but I don't **know why**

About the author

Deborah Marshall-Warren is a hypnotherapist who has run her own private practice, *Whole-Being Interactive Hypnotherapy,* for eight years — conducting hundreds of interactive one-to-one sessions over that period. Deborah was formerly a teacher of sixteen to nineteen-year-olds at a college in East London. An interest in writing, and the creation of teaching materials for her young students led her five years on, to develop a freelance role as a designer of interactive instructional materials for corporations in the UK before following her heart and the callings of her intuition into a career as a hypnotherapist some six years later.

She holds a Post Graduate Certificate in Education, a Diploma in Hypnotherapy and is a Emeritus Fellow of The Hypnotherapy Society (FHS Emeritus), and a Fellow of The Royal Society for the Promotion of Health. Deborah is a long-standing advisor to the editorial staff and features department at *Here's Health,* magazine, a leading complementary health magazine.

Her professional experience has been wide-ranging: she has treated a very great variety of requests for help and healing. As well as publishing articles and contributing to them, she is regularly asked to provide information and guidance to journalists seeking to find out more about hypnotherapy and its effectiveness in specified areas. She has spoken about her work on television and frequently participates in radio broadcasts as a subject expert. Broadcasts have included both local and national radio.

Deborah is the author of *Mind Detox* book and audiotape published by Thorsons in 1999 as well as *I'm Afraid of Hypnosis, but I Don't Know Why* and *Interactive Hypnotherapy: A Practical Training Manual* for practitioners in the field published by Whole-Being Books in 2003.

Useful Names and Addresses

Whole-Being Interactive Hypnotherapy
c/o 155 Sumatra Road
West Hampstead
London NW6 1PN
Tel: +44 (0)20 7432 0307
Fax: +44 (0)70 3115 0396
email: appointments@marshall-warren.com
www.marshall-warren.com
National Independent Provider Organisation Code: 8G894

To find a practising interactive hypnotherapist in the U.K. please contact:
The Hypnotherapy Society (HS)
The Society for Practising Hypnotherapists
Honorary President: C.F. Stossel FRCS(Ed.) FRCS(Eng.) FRSM FBOA
BCM HYPSOC
London WC1 3XX
Tel: +44 (0)845 6024585
email: hs@easynet.co.uk
www.hypnotherapysociety.com

The Royal Society for the Promotion of Health
38A St. George's Drive
London SW1V 4BH
Tel: +44 (0)20 7630 0121
Email: rshealth@rshealth.org.uk
www.rsph.org
Established 1876 **Patron:** Her Majesty the Queen

The Foundation for Integrated Medicine
International House
59 Compton Road
London N1 2YT
Tel: +44 (0)20 7688 1881

Department of Health
Complementary Therapies Unit
Wellington House
133-155 Waterloo Road
London SE1 8UG
Tel: +44 (0)20 7972 2000

Organisation Codes Service, Department of Health
ISDN4A
380D Skipton House
80 London Road
Elephant and Castle
London SE1 6LH
Tel: 020 7972 6051
Fax: 020 7972 6538
(*Practitioners who wish to register as an independent service provider and be
allocated a National Independent Provider Organisation Code may write to this
organisation. For public access to the provider directory:
www.doh.gov.uk/codes/*)

The Royal Society of Medicine
Section of Hypnosis & Psychosomatic Medicine
1 Wimpole Street
London W1G 0AE
Tel: +44 (0)20 7290 2986
Fax: +44 (0)20 7290 2989

British Society of Medical and Dental Hypnosis
27 Broadlands Heights
53/58 Broadlands Avenue
Edgware HA8 8PF
The Referral Secretary
Tel: +44 (0)20 8905 4342

Professor John Gruzelier
Department of Cognitive Neuroscience and Behaviour
Imperial College of Science, Technology and Medicine
St. Dunstan's Road
London
W6 8RF
Tel: +44 (0)20 8846 7246
Fax: +44 (0) 20 8846 1670
Email: j.gruzelier@ic.ac.uk

British United Provident Association (BUPA)
BUPA House
15-19 Bloomsbury Way
London WC1A 2BA
Tel: +44 (0)20 7656 2000
http://www.bupa.com

Hypnotherapy training providers:-

Whole-Being Interactive Hypnotherapy
For recently trained, and practising hypnotherapists
Master Classes in Malta
For more information: www.marshall-warren.com
email: appointments@marshall-warren.com

The Hypnotherapy Society (HS)
For a comprehensive list of recommended training providers
meeting National Occupational Standards for Hypnotherapy.
www.hypnotherapysociety.com

NSPCC (London)
4th Floor, 168-172 Old Street
London EC1V 9BP
Tel: 24 hour service on 0808 800 5000
www.nspcc.org.uk

Other organisations of interest:-

Mind
The Mental Health Charity
15-19 Broadway
London E15 4BQ
Tel: +44(0)20-8519 2122
MindInfoLine: +44(0)845-7660163
Local Groups: +44 (0)20 8519 2122
email: info@mind.org.uk
www.mind.org.uk

Thrive
Beech Hill
Berkshire RG7 2AT
Tel: +44(0)118-988 5688
email: info@thrive.org.uk
www.thrive.org.uk
(using gardening to change lives)

Brahma Kumaris World Spiritual University
Global Co-operation House
65 Pound Lane
London
NW10 2HH
Tel: +44(0)20 8459 1400

The Brahma Kumaris offer Meditation, Stress Management and Positive Thinking courses throughout the UK. Books, tapes and CDs are available from BK publications at the address above.

Advertising Standards Authority
2 Torrington Place
London WC1E 7HW
Tel: +44(0)20-7580 5555
Fax: +44(0)20-7631 3051
www.asa.org.uk

I'm **afraid** of **hypnosis**   but I don't **know why**

Appendix: Hypnotherapy Society Code of Ethics

Listed below are some extracts from the Code of Ethics of the Hypnotherapy Society, reproduced with the Society's permission. For the full and up-to-date code, please refer to the Society's web site, www.hypnotherapysociety.com. This Code of Ethics was developed from the British Association of Counselling and Psychotherapy (BACP) Code of Ethics of April 2002.

- Good practice involves clarifying and agreeing the rights and responsibilities of both the practitioner and client at appropriate points in their working relationship.

- Dual relationships arise when the practitioner has two or more kinds of relationship concurrently with a client, for example client and trainee, friend and client, colleague and supervisee. The existence of a dual relationship with a client is seldom neutral and can have a powerful beneficial or detrimental impact that may not always be easily foreseeable. For these reasons practitioners are required to consider the implications of entering into dual relationships with clients, to avoid entering into relationships that are likely to be detrimental to clients, and to be readily accountable to clients and colleagues for any dual relationships that occur.

- Practitioners are encouraged to keep adequate records of their work with clients unless there are sound reasons for not doing so. All records should be accurate, respectful of clients and colleagues and protected from unauthorised disclosure. Practitioners should take into account their responsibilities and their client's rights under data protection legislation and any other legal requirements.

- Practitioners are required to keep up to date with the latest knowledge and respond to changing circumstances. They should consider carefully their own need for continuing professional development and engage in appropriate educational activities.

- The practice of hypnotherapy depends on gaining and honouring the trust of clients. Keeping trust requires:

  - attentiveness to the quality of listening and respect offered to clients
  - culturally appropriate ways of communicating that are courteous and clear
  - respect for privacy and dignity
  - clear explanation of the role, type and scope of hypnotherapy to be utilised
  - careful attention to client consent and confidentiality

- Clients should be adequately informed about the nature of the services being offered. Practitioners should obtain adequately informed consent from their clients and respect a client's right to withdraw at any point.

- Practitioners should ensure that services are normally delivered on the basis of the client's explicit consent. Reliance on implicit consent is more vulnerable to misunderstandings and is best avoided unless there are sound reasons for doing so. Overriding a client's known wishes or consent is a serious matter that requires commensurate justification. Practitioners should be prepared to be readily accountable to clients and colleagues if they override a client's known wishes.

- Respecting client confidentiality is a fundamental requirement for keeping trust. The professional management of confidentiality concerns the protection of personally identifiable and sensitive information from unauthorised disclosure. Disclosure may be authorised by client consent or the law. Any disclosures should be undertaken in ways that best protect the client's trust. Practitioners should be willing to be accountable to their clients and to their profession for their management of confidentiality in general and particularly for any disclosures made without their client's consent.

- Practitioners should normally be willing to respond to their client's requests for information about the way that they are working and any assessment that they may have made. This professional requirement does not apply if it is considered that imparting this information would be detrimental to the client or inconsistent with the hypnotherapeutic approach previously agreed with the client. Clients may have legal rights to this information and these need to be taken into account.

- Practitioners should not allow their professional relationships with clients to be prejudiced by any personal views they may hold about lifestyle, gender, age, disability, race, sexual orientation, beliefs or culture.

- Practitioners should not conduct inductions by telephone or any other medium save face to face contact; excepting only induction tapes or other audio media provided to clients with a printed list of instructions for appropriate usage.

- Practitioners should not conduct stage hypnosis.

- All practitioners are encouraged to share their professional knowledge and practice in order to benefit their clients and the public.
- Practitioners should respond promptly and appropriately to any complaint received from their clients.
- Particular care should be taken over the integrity of presenting qualifications, accreditation, and professional standing.
- The title "Dr" may be used as a practitioner only where (a) the title holder is a UK registered medical practitioner in good standing or (b) where a non-medical doctorate is held, the practitioner can demonstrate that the doctorate is a qualification relevant to the practice of hypnotherapy. Doctorates in psychology, psychotherapy, counselling, and hypnotherapy are specifically included in (b). The practitioner should seek clarification and written approval from the Society for use of the title "Dr" as a practitioner in all cases. (c) If the title "Dr" is approved by the Society and the practitioner is a non-medical doctor, this must be made explicit in all literature relevant to the practitioner's practice; furthermore, each client must be specifically made aware that the practitioner is not medically qualified.